The Dragonflies of Sussex

A guide to their distribution and conservation

P.A. Belden
V.J. Downer
J.C. Luck
H.D.V. Prendergast
D. Sadler

With a Foreword by
Prof. Chris Baines

BDS

Essedon Press
for the
Sussex Group
British Dragonfly Society

Printed in Slovenia for Compass Press
Designed by Blacker Design, East Grinstead, W. Sussex RH19 4LY
Published by Essedon Press, Spylaws, Wych Cross, Forest Row, E. Sussex RH18 5JP

ISBN 0-9525549-1-7
First published 2004, revised and reprinted 2005

Contents

Foreword

Dragonflies. Even the name is full of magic! Watch them in flight. One second they are hovering, motionless. The next they are hunting at high speed. How do they do that? Even more amazingly, how does a creature that spends half its life in the muddy bottom of a pond or stream, all legs and jaws and menace, transform itself into an elegant and aerobatic flying machine before your very eyes?

On warm sunny summer's days I can sit beside my garden pond, and watch a wildlife spectacular which is as impressive as anything beamed in to my living room from the Serengeti or the South American rainforest. I never tire of watching dragonfly larvae as they leave the relative safety of the water, stretch in the sunshine, and struggle out of their tight-fitting pond-wear for the final time.

As the limp, bedraggled insect slowly pumps its wings and prepares to fly, it is all too obvious why so many of these creatures are now under threat. As larvae they are more vulnerable than most to chemical pollution. They also need a mix of habitats, which may range from open water, through marginal wetland vegetation to the wider hunting grounds of hedgerow, woodland edge and open wildflower meadow, and of course they need an environment that can support the pond life and the other flying insects upon which our dragonflies depend for food.

Now, these spectacular creatures face another threat. As climate change begins to gather pace, there is concern that some species, including dragonflies, will fail to adapt fast enough. We need to rebuild a landscape, in the towns as well as in the countryside, where wetlands, woodlands, grasslands, rivers and canals are linked together, so that wildlife can move more successfully from place to place. This means adopting more creative conservation measures: caring for existing habitats but also making new ones. For some species that can be difficult, but many kinds of dragonflies respond extremely well to habitat creation, and the more new habitat they have, the better.

This book is bound to fill you with admiration for the beauty of these wonderful insects - but it must do more. If future generations are to share the magic of miraculous summer's day displays, then the book must inspire you to action. Dig a garden pond or two. Campaign for canal conservation and for cleaner rivers, and encourage everyone you know to enjoy watching dragonflies.

Chris Baines
May 2004

Its southerly position and proximity to continental Europe help make Sussex one of Britain's richest counties for dragonflies. So far 39 species have been recorded. One caught in 1818 has never been seen in Britain again; one became extinct in the county soon after World War Two; four have occurred as occasional visitors; four have just one or two old records; and 29 are resident. This picture is likely to change, especially with climate change.

Never before has there been such popular interest in these large and colourful insects. Thanks to new guide-books they are easy to identify and anyone with binoculars can follow their flights of unsurpassed agility. The building of garden ponds has also brought dragonflies into the heart of our towns and cities, while few children on school pond-dipping trips may easily forget the predatory larvae and their miraculous metamorphosis into winged beauties.

Alongside this growing enthusiasm for the natural world has come another good reason to study our dragonflies. They are excellent indicators of the state of water in our environment: in streams and rivers, ponds, lakes and reservoirs, and even the ditches that divide up fields and meadows. They help us to gauge the health of all these wetlands, and to judge the success or failure of our managing and protecting them.

Our first aim in this book is to summarise what we know about the distribution of dragonflies in Sussex today and to further the conservation of where they live. As the maps show, we still lack a complete picture for even our most abundant species and we do not always understand why others are rare. However, the maps do offer a baseline of information against which we can record and analyse changes in distribution as species respond to environmental conditions that themselves seldom stay still. Conserving our dragonflies will help us to conserve the Sussex environment as well.

Our second aim is to encourage you to go looking for dragonflies, to record them, and to submit your observations so that gaps in the maps can be filled, the changes noted, and new arrivals on our shores recorded. It will be a fun task – and a very useful one!

A fossil species: *Libellulium zdrzaleki*, from Lower Weald Clay, Rudgwick Brickworks, from 140–100 million years ago

2 The Sussex scene

Dragonflies are essentially insects of freshwater, living underwater for most of their lives as larvae, and only free of it for a relatively short time as free-flying adults. The larvae of each species have their own particular requirements for the temperature range, acidity, and oxygen content of water, and for the amount of submerged and emergent plant life. They have varying tolerance of pollution. As adults, dragonflies require areas suitable for hunting – often well away from water – for resting, and most importantly for mating and egg-laying.

Freshwater habitats in Sussex can be broadly categorised as watercourses draining grassland (typically rivers, brooks and levels); fens and reedbeds; and bodies of standing water ranging in size from large reservoirs to tiny heathland pools and urban ponds.

The main county landscapes have their own characteristic habitats and dragonfly species.

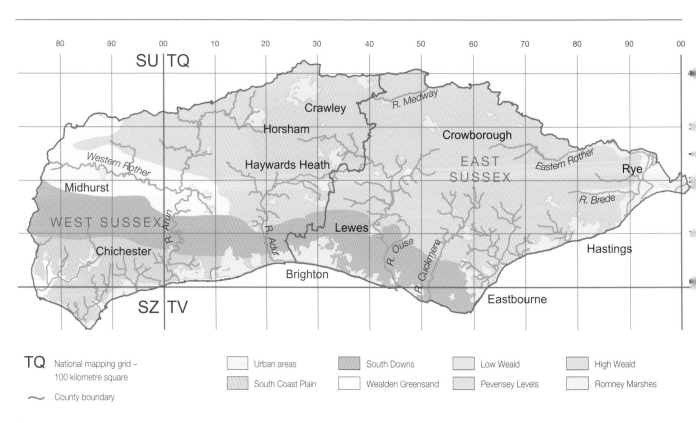

TQ	National mapping grid – 100 kilometre square		Urban areas		South Downs		Low Weald		High Weald
~	County boundary		South Coast Plain		Wealden Greensand		Pevensey Levels		Romney Marshes

The main county landscapes

The High Weald, made up of clays and sandstones, has well-wooded, steep-sided stream valleys that were often dammed by the iron industry to make hammer ponds. It contains the acid heaths and bogs of Ashdown Forest and most of the county's large reservoirs such as Ardingly, Bewl and Weirwood.

The Low Weald is composed of highly impermeable clay, with many small ponds and tributary streams.

Pevensey Levels and **Romney Marshes** are coastal wetlands, criss-crossed with freshwater ditches.

The Wealden Greensand contains the key inland wetland complex of Amberley and Pulborough Brooks on the River Arun.

The South Downs, a ridge of chalk, is essentially waterless, bar a few remaining dew ponds that are vital oases for wildlife.

The South Coast Plain, composed of clays, sands and gravels, has many gravel pits and ponds but is highly urbanised.

Most of the main rivers of Sussex drain southwards into the Channel. From west to east they are the Arun (joined near Pulborough by the western Rother) that meets the sea at Littlehampton, the Adur (Shoreham), the Ouse (Newhaven), and the Cuckmere (near Seaford). The Brede flows east to join the eastern Rother, reaching the sea below Rye. In the north of the county the Medway drains into Kent. These rivers are fed by many tributaries and there are a number of smaller and winterborne streams, such as the Lavant that runs to the sea via Chichester.

The sea and estuaries, being saline or brackish, are unsuitable for dragonflies.

Sussex has some significant conurbations and numerous large towns, where the vast majority of people live. Far from being waterless they contain many garden ponds that are important for attracting insects, including dragonflies. Their creation and management have helped offset the terrible loss of ponds in the countryside which, due to changing farming practices and the piping of water, are now largely redundant.

3 Dragonfly recording

A quarter of a century has passed since the last Sussex-wide survey of dragonflies was produced by D. Chelmick (Chelmick 1979). It provides not only an invaluable baseline against which the results of this survey can be compared, but also a summary of the history of dragonfly recording in the county up to that time.

The first key work for recording in Sussex was *Libellulinae observed in Sussex, chiefly in the neighbourhood of Lewes* by W. Unwin (Unwin 1853). His records were republished by Mrs Merrifield (1860) and merged with subsequent records by the Reverend E. Bloomfield of Guestling (Bloomfield 1900). Both he and W. Lucas, a Surrey schoolteacher and renowned amateur naturalist of the time, made contributions on dragonflies in the natural history section of *The Victoria County History of Sussex* (Lucas and Bloomfield 1905). Lucas also produced the first authoritative British publication on dragonflies (Lucas 1900).

By the start of the twentieth century, East Sussex was generally better studied than West Sussex, apart from some work by H. Turner who provided some records from the Liphook area (Chelmick 1979). However, the naturalist H. Guermonprez had made extensive collections (including 550 dragonfly specimens), spanning more than 40 years, of his many natural history interests throughout West Sussex. This collection formed the basis of the Bognor Regis Museum in 1943 and was moved to Portsmouth Museum in 1972 (where it still resides). Surprisingly, and despite editing a column called Selborne Notes in *The West Sussex Gazette* from 1906 to 1924, he published very little in the way of records.

Recording in East Sussex received a boost with the appearance of reports in *The Hastings and East Sussex Naturalist* (*HESN*), first published in 1906. In 1922 A. Craven, a naturalist with interests including conchology (snails) and ornithology (birds), published a list of Sussex dragonflies (Craven 1922). Subsequent significant publications were two by Capt. T. Dannreuther, *The dragonflies of East Sussex* (Dannreuther 1939) and *Dragonflies of West Sussex* (Dannreuther 1945), the latter rather less comprehensive, but it did include an appraisal of the Guermonprez collection. As Honorary Secretary of the Insect Immigration Committee of the South-Eastern Union of Scientific Societies, he also published a note on dragonfly migration (Dannreuther 1941), a topic that once again is of great interest. H. Attlee was one of the few regular recorders in East Sussex in the 1930s and 1940s and he was joined in the immediate post war years in the area by N. Moore (now one of the world's foremost authorities on dragonfly conservation). They were both regular contributors of records to *HESN*.

Little notable recording then took place until the Sussex Trust for Nature Conservation (now Sussex Wildlife Trust) commissioned a systematic survey of the status of dragonflies across the county. Preliminary work was started by C. Haes in 1965 but the project was taken over by D. Chelmick in 1971, effectively completed in 1976, and a report produced in 1979 (Chelmick 1979). Building on this report, with the aim of producing a more comprehensive and up to date account, the current Sussex Dragonfly Survey was started in 1989 by two local conservationists, P. Belden (who had already surveyed the Pevensey Levels; Belden 1987) and J. Halls.

Through an informal network of volunteers, knowledge of the distribution of dragonflies in the county gradually built up. At each summer's end a map was produced of all sightings, together with individual species maps. These spurred on the next year's dragonfly explorations. In 1994 the formation of the Sussex Group of the British Dragonfly Society (BDS) gave the survey more impetus. Two years later J. Knight took over the position of County Recorder, and V. Downer began to computerise all the records, hitherto held on cards. These are now all held electronically by the Sussex Biodiversity Record Centre (SxBRC) at the Sussex Wildlife Trust headquarters at Woods Mill near Henfield. It is their system that has produced the distribution maps used here. By 2003 J. Luck had become the County Recorder, with the tasks of liaising with the SxBRC and encouraging people to continue to record the distribution of dragonflies across Sussex.

Depending on their experience, surveyors could submit records of any of the stages of the dragonfly's life: as larvae, exuviae (the spent cases of larvae that have emerged from the water to become adults) and the adults themselves, plus evidence of breeding (mating pairs and egg-laying). The recommended form of recording has been the standard RA70 card, supplied by the Biological Records Centre at Monks Wood, and, in appropriate circumstances, the RA74 Migrant Recording Card for species arriving from abroad and for unusual movements within Britain. The nationwide use of these cards helped to ensure standardised recording methods and to improve information about the distribution, numbers and habitat requirements for each species. Now (2004) automated input on Species Recorder software is available from SxBRC, where records are sent after validation by the recorder.

Further development in 2005 has resulted in Odonata Recorder being available in place of Species Recorder, providing a customised version for dragonfly recorders.

A good example of the influence of the accumulating data is our work on the River Arun, helping to protect and conserve our richest dragonfly river. They were used to guide engineering works (e.g. Pallingham Weir) and to respond to planning applications (such as successfully preventing a large green waste plant by the river near Billingshurst). They also contributed to the long-term restoration plans for the Wey and Arun Canal (Ryland 1994), to propose sites for protective designations and conservation management, with information being passed to the Farming and Wildlife Advisory Group and for a comprehensive report for the Arun Valley Project (Belden 1999).

Now that the data are stored electronically at the Sussex Biodiversity Record Centre, they can be interrogated and collated in many different ways, and used to produce outputs such as the maps in this book. They can also be combined with a wealth of other wildlife information to defend sites or to enhance management of the wetland habitats of Sussex, all for the benefit of dragonflies and other fauna and flora.

The data in this book far exceed what were available for Chelmick (1979). From the 1965–1978 survey he had records of 'probable breeding' from only 309 (29%) of the ca. 1067 tetrads (2x2 kilometre squares) of Sussex. We have been able to map at the fourfold

greater resolution of 1x1 kilometre squares (a total of 4047) and have received records from 1649 of them (41%). From pre 1989 there are 5058 records of Odonata in Sussex; this survey has added a further 34,551. This increase is reflected by figures for the commoner species: 490 (pre 1989) and 2255 (post 1989) for the Azure Damselfly; 290 and 1417 for the Brown Hawker; and 268 and 2397 for the Common Darter. The increase may be less dramatic for scarcer species (e.g. 181 and 524 for the Hairy Dragonfly) and for those with restricted distribution (e.g. 134 and 216 for the Variable Damselfly). A glance at many of the maps and the one on p.11 will show that, although parts of the county like Pevensey Levels are well covered (and indicate the presence of diligent and enthusiastic observers), there are still large and notable gaps. Those on the Downs may well reflect an absence of dragonflies (and suitable habitats), but there are other gaps (for example in the northwest of the county) that indicate that our coverage of Sussex is still by no means complete.

Resident species

Dragonflies belong to the Order of insects known as the Odonata (literally 'the toothed ones'). The Odonata comprise two Sub-orders. The Anisoptera ('unequal wings') are what most people would describe as true dragonflies – large, stout, fast-flying, and perching with their wings held straight out from the sides – whereas the Zygoptera ('similar wings') are the more dainty, weaker-flying damselflies that tend to fold their wings over their 'backs' when perched.

The sequence of species we use here is used by the BDS (see Section 9 for details of its website).

Each species account begins with a brief introduction highlighting any key identification and behavioural features and is then divided into a number of headings. For a detailed description, for example on how to distinguish between species, sexes, and young and old insects, you will need an identification guide-book (see Section 9).

National status
Is the distribution of the species in Britain, based on information held on the website of the BDS.

Status in Sussex
Summarises the abundance of species in the county (i.e. both East and West Sussex).

Distributions are shown on the maps, where the dots represent 1 kilometre squares where species have been recorded. The open dots represent pre-1989 records, i.e. before the start of our 1989–2003 survey. For the survey, the black dots indicate where species have simply been seen, and the red ones where there has been evidence of breeding and, therefore, the presence of suitable habitat.

The *Sussex Rare Species Inventory* (maintained by the SxBRC) highlights those that are scarce at local level.

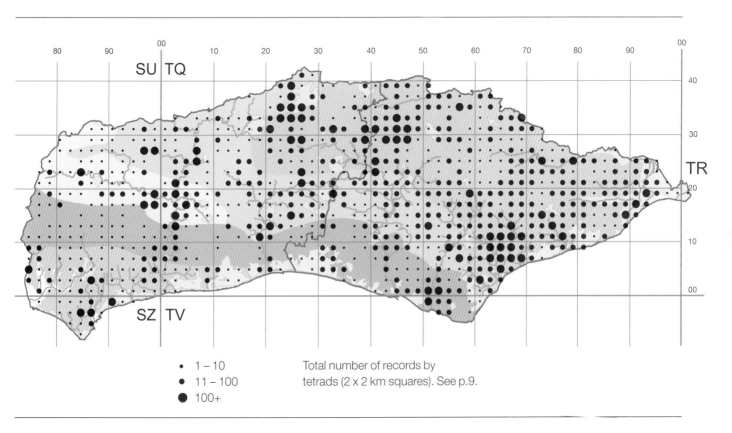

		1 – 10	Total number of records by
	•	11 – 100	tetrads (2 x 2 km squares). See p.9.
	●	100+	

Habitat

Summarises the habitat needs or characteristics of each species, complementing the landscape types of the county highlighted by the maps.

Flight times

Describes the period during which adult dragonflies are on the wing in Sussex, often a useful feature for distinguishing between similar-looking species. In some years, earlier or later times may be recorded, for example if there is an early spring or Indian summer.

Historical records

Summarises our knowledge of past records of the species in Sussex, with particular emphasis on those that show a significant difference from what we currently know (for example about their range or abundance).

Conservation

Highlights particular issues affecting each species. Section 6 covers the topic at county level.

Beautiful Demoiselle
Calopteryx virgo

This aptly named, exotic-looking damselfly is our only one with wholly coloured wings. The metallic blue-green male has dark black-brown wings with a blue iridescence. The metallic greenish-bronze female has light brown wings. The dancing, butterfly-like flight is a distinctive feature as it flits over clean, fast-flowing streams.

► Male
▼ Female

National status
Locally abundant. Mostly found south-west of a line between Liverpool and Folkestone.

Status in Sussex
Widespread across the county except for the Downs and southwards. Chelmick (1979) noted that this species was "extremely rare on the Weald Clay". Although still uncommon, our survey shows evidence of this species right across the Low Weald at suitable sites. The distribution across the Wealden Greensand shows a similar pattern in both accounts, but there is a greater abundance and coverage in our maps here, probably due to the greater survey effort.

▲ Shady stream,
Ashdown Forest

◄ Mating

Habitat
Fast-flowing water with a stony bottom and abundant bankside vegetation, typically alders.

Flight times
Late May – early September.

Historical records
Lucas and Bloomfield (1905) recorded a similar distribution to our current survey data, but the species was considered quite rare in the Hastings area in the 1880s (Dannreuther 1939).

N. Moore (in Chelmick 1979) thought it to be "fairly common" on the tributaries of the River Brede but our data suggest it has either declined or is under-recorded there.

Conservation
This species is highly sensitive to pollution, hence its patchy distribution across the county. The Low Weald, where the characteristic small fields and tree-lined streams are still in evidence, is its stronghold.

However, the species does need open, sunny glades so neglected riverbanks, where the overhanging vegetation has taken over completely, are unsuitable. The species has been lost where more intensive farming has developed.

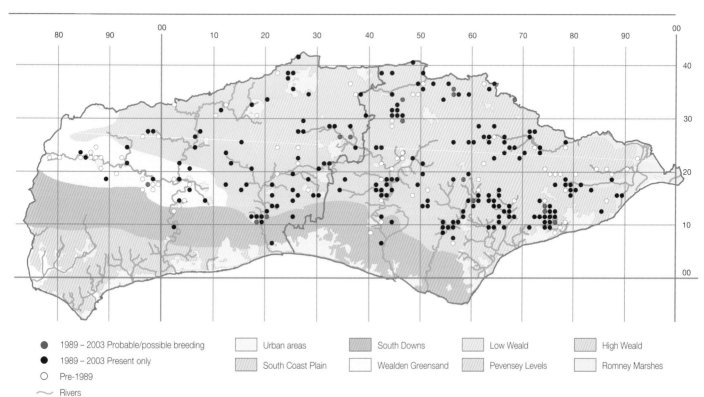

- ● 1989 – 2003 Probable/possible breeding
- ● 1989 – 2003 Present only
- ○ Pre-1989
- ~ Rivers

- Urban areas
- South Coast Plain
- South Downs
- Wealden Greensand
- Low Weald
- Pevensey Levels
- High Weald
- Romney Marshes

Banded Demoiselle
Calopteryx splendens

▼ Male

The striking male, with its brilliant kingfisher-blue body, has deep blue-banded wings that create a fluttering, helicopter-like flight over slow-flowing streams and rivers. The female is metallic green becoming bronze with age; the wings are translucent with a green tinge. The two demoiselles are our largest damselflies and the most impressive in their colouration and graceful flight. Where they occur in the same places, the Banded Demoiselle tends to be the more dominant.

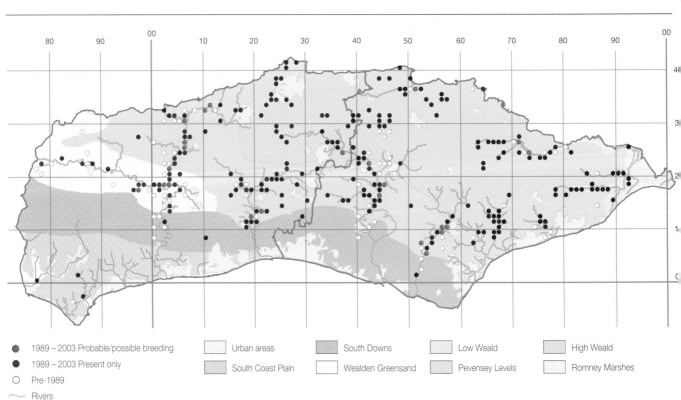

- ● 1989 – 2003 Probable/possible breeding
- ● 1989 – 2003 Present only
- ○ Pre-1989
- ~ Rivers

- Urban areas
- South Coast Plain
- South Downs
- Wealden Greensand
- Low Weald
- Pevensey Levels
- High Weald
- Romney Marshes

◀ River Arun at New Bridge

▼ Female

National status
Common in most of England and Wales.

Status in Sussex
Locally common north of the Downs, most notably along the River Arun, but with a limited distribution along the western Rother and absent from certain areas of both the High and Low Weald.

Habitat
Almost always slow-moving, muddy-bottomed streams, rivers and canals, with open meadow habitat.

Flight times
Mid May – early September.

Historical records
Despite the different habitat requirements to the Beautiful Demoiselle, the comments made for that species can also generally be applied to this one, except in the far east of the county. Craven (1922) added just a single record of his own for that area and Chelmick (1979) noted its absence from the Brede and the lower stretches of the eastern Rother. However, our survey results show that this species may have expanded its range in the far east.

Conservation
This species is found at some of our key unpolluted sites. It hugs the upper reaches of our main rivers and streams and it can occur in large numbers in sympathetically managed habitats such as traditional meadows. Sensitive water management is necessary in order to maintain healthy emergent vegetation. Adjacent meadows are useful feeding and roosting grounds.

Emerald Damselfly

Lestes sponsa

▼ Male   Mating ▶

This species has the uncharacteristic habit for a damselfly of resting with its wings outstretched, typically in a half-open position. It is very hard to distinguish from its relative, the Scarce Emerald (*Lestes dryas*), but this species is now, sadly, extinct in Sussex. The male is largely metallic green, but the tip and base of the abdomen are pale blue. The female is a duller green and lacks the pale blue segments.

Female ▶

National status
Locally common throughout Britain.

Status in Sussex
Scattered across the county, with concentrations on Pevensey Levels, Romney Marsh and Ashdown Forest. Chelmick (1979) referred to a "marked preference for sandstone regions and presumably more acid waters", but our survey shows a broader, albeit scattered and patchy distribution.

Habitat
A wide range of shallow, standing waters, from acid heathland bogs to canals, ponds and lakesides, as long as there is plenty of aquatic and marginal vegetation. It also tolerates fairly brackish sites.

Flight times
Late June – late September.

Historical records
It appears that this species has always had a widespread distribution, and our current map shows a similar pattern to that of Chelmick (1979), though with additional sites and a wider range of habitats.

Conservation
The best Sussex sites contain plenty of submerged and floating vegetation. Since fish are major predators, the larvae need sufficient plant cover or, preferably, water bodies without fish in them. The adults usually mate amongst lush vegetation cover around water; the female, sometimes completely submerged, inserts her eggs into plant stems. The patchy distribution is at least partly explained by such specialist habitat requirements, which could be easily destroyed through excessive clearance or dredging.

▼ River Arun near Billingshurst

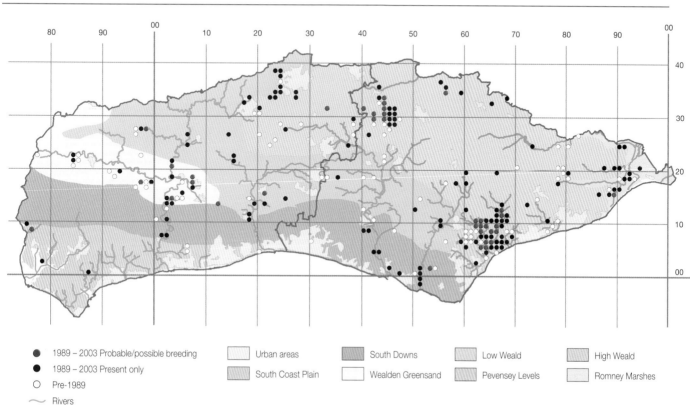

- ● 1989 – 2003 Probable/possible breeding
- ● 1989 – 2003 Present only
- ○ Pre-1989
- ～ Rivers

Urban areas

South Coast Plain

South Downs

Wealden Greensand

Low Weald

Pevensey Levels

High Weald

Romney Marshes

White-legged Damselfly
Platycnemis pennipes

Female ▶
▼ Male

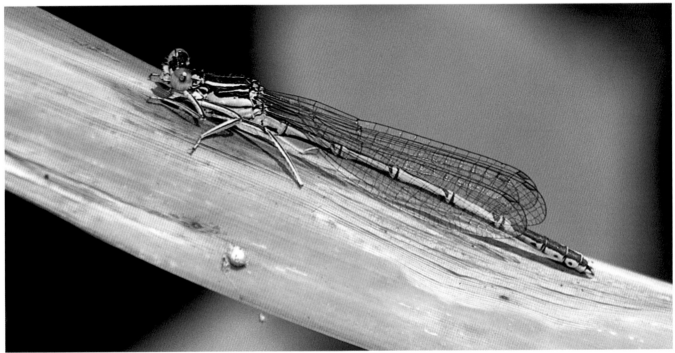

This very pale-coloured damselfly – teneral insects are off-white and look like flying matchsticks, the male is blue with distinctive creamy-white legs and the female is green – is found in a limited number of places in Sussex. Where it does occur, however, typically in slow-flowing rivers, it can occur in abundance. It is a good pollution indicator.

National status
Uncommon south of a line from the Wash, though can be locally abundant.

Status in Sussex
Predominantly found across the High and Low Weald, where it can be locally abundant, and well distributed along sections of the upper Arun and mid-Sussex Adur. There is an isolated presence at Chichester gravel pits. It is listed in the *Sussex Rare Species Inventory*.

Habitat
Unpolluted and well-vegetated, slow-moving rivers and streams; occasionally in lakes and ponds. Chelmick (1979) made the point about two distinct habitats: rivers on the (Low) Weald Clay, and lakes with streams on the Ashdown Beds (High Weald). This pattern is evident on our map, though recent records have added further sites, which makes this split a little too simplistic. An interesting feature of this species in Sussex (as has been reported elsewhere; see Cham 2003) is its occurrence on lakes and ponds. Research is needed to determine the apparent significance of this preference.

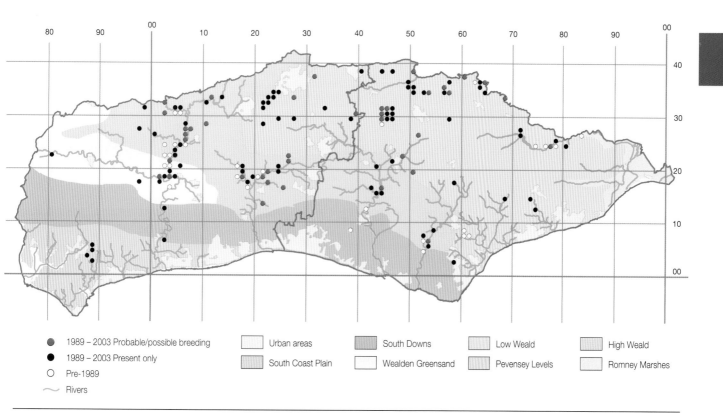

- ● 1989 – 2003 Probable/possible breeding
- ● 1989 – 2003 Present only
- ○ Pre-1989
- ~ Rivers

Urban areas
South Coast Plain
South Downs
Wealden Greensand
Low Weald
Pevensey Levels
High Weald
Romney Marshes

Immature ▶

▼ Females ovipositing while in tandem with males

suggests that either it has been under-recorded, or it may be extending its range. For example, Chelmick (1979) found no trace of the species on the eastern Rother, where it now occurs, although it certainly cannot be described as "plentiful" as he mentioned it was in the 1930s and 1940s.

Flight times
Late May – mid August.

Historical records
Unwin (1853) reported seeing a single specimen on the Lewes Downs in 1849. Chelmick (1979) suggested that its usual haunts were the Arun, Adur and Cuckmere. He also pointed out that this species has otherwise been absent from the Ouse, but our survey confirms its presence in the Low Weald section. Dannreuther (1939) mentioned only three or four recorded below Robertsbridge on the river Rother in 1931–1932 by H. Attlee. The wider distribution shown now by our survey

Conservation
Vulnerable to pollution, this species has its strongholds in Sussex where there is plentiful mature vegetation and clean flowing waters. Insensitive or extensive vegetation clearance is a threat. Chelmick (1979) noted that the White-legged Damselfly can occur in large numbers on fields surrounding lakes and rivers. Any such fields adjacent to our larger water-bodies should therefore be incorporated into conservation management plans.

Large Red Damselfly
Pyrrhosoma nymphula

▼ Male

The first damselfly of the year to emerge, it can appear as early as April in warm conditions (the first 2004 record was on 16 April on a ditch by the Cuckmere at Alfriston). It is very common throughout Sussex, living in a wide variety of habitats, and is an early coloniser of new ponds. The male is predominantly red with black legs and black bands on the base of the abdomen. The female occurs in three forms with varying degrees of black on the abdomen.

▼ Male

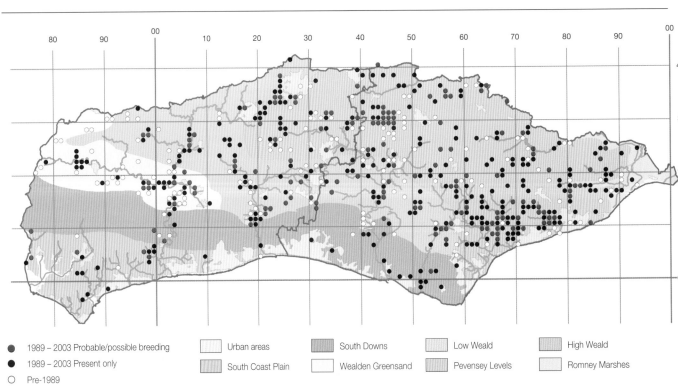

● 1989 – 2003 Probable/possible breeding

● 1989 – 2003 Present only

○ Pre-1989

∼ Rivers

☐ Urban areas

☐ South Coast Plain

☐ South Downs

☐ Wealden Greensand

☐ Low Weald

☐ Pevensey Levels

☐ High Weald

☐ Romney Marshes

National status
Widespread and common in Britain.

Status in Sussex
Common. Very well distributed over the county, found almost anywhere there are suitable water bodies. Chelmick (1979) noted it being most abundant on "sluggish acid streams and seepages" which is affirmed by the cluster of records on Ashdown Forest for example, but our survey also gives prominence to the clay country of the Low Weald.

Habitat
A wide range, from ponds, lakes and canals to the quieter stretches of fast-flowing streams and rivers.

Flight times
Usually the first species to be on the wing. Late April – early September.

Historical records
All old accounts regarded this species as widespread throughout the county, although Chelmick's survey (1979) considered it virtually absent from the coastal plain. Our survey indicates some colonisation of the coastal area, though a look at his map and ours shows similarities in the abundance of the Large Red as one moves inland.

Conservation
Cursory observation shows this to be a very common species across the county, but more detailed study reveals an absence in areas of intensive agriculture. For example, although it occurs in most grid squares for the Pevensey Levels, its greatest concentrations and the most evidence of breeding are in the more traditional grazing meadows, with a marked decline or absence in the pump-drained, arable areas.

▶ Mating

Red-eyed Damselfly
Erythromma najas

The blue 'tail' to a greenish-black abdomen and unmistakable bright, blood-red eyes single out the male. The female is less red-eyed than the male and lacks the blue-tipped abdomen. The species is characteristically found on lily pads in the middle of a pond or lake – so using binoculars is a great help.

National status
Locally common in south-east England and the Welsh Borders. Of late, there has been an expansion in range to the west and north.

Status in Sussex
Locally common across the county with a concentration on the Pevensey Levels. Fairly well distributed across the Low Weald, but more patchy in the High Weald and Wealden Greensand.

▼ Male

◄ Female, with pr

◀ Lake at Sheffield Park Gardens

Habitat
Lakes and large ponds with plenty of floating vegetation such as water lilies; also on quiet stretches of rivers and canals.

Flight times
Mid May – late August.

Historical records
This is one of several species first recorded in Sussex on 29 August 1908 at a site near Tunbridge Wells by E. Speyer (Bloomfield 1910). Dannreuther (1939) described it as "fairly rare even where it breeds". It was not until the 1940s that this species was regularly recorded by N. Moore (Chelmick 1979). There seems to have been a recent increase, possibly due to migration, being recorded for the first time at Castle Water in 1997 (Rye Harbour Report 1999), and at Icklesham in August 2002 (after the influx of Small Red-eyed Damselfly [p. 24] had been noted; Hunter 2003).

Conservation
On still-water bodies, it is important to maintain large areas of floating vegetation, such as water lilies and pondweeds, that are used by territorial males, and marginal vegetation favoured by females and mating pairs. Meandering watercourses with slacks and other calm stretches that can be colonised by floating vegetation are ideal habitats. These can be destroyed by engineering activities (such as canalisation) designed to increase water flow. The restoration of the Shopham Loop on the western Rother will help this species.

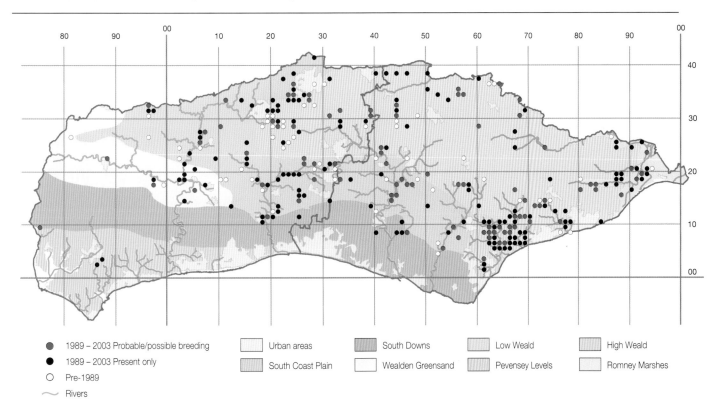

● 1989 – 2003 Probable/possible breeding
● 1989 – 2003 Present only
○ Pre-1989
〜 Rivers

Urban areas
South Coast Plain
South Downs
Wealden Greensand
Low Weald
Pevensey Levels
High Weald
Romney Marshes

Small Red-eyed Damselfly
Erythromma viridulum

This species, new to Sussex, may present an initial challenge to distinguish it from the well-established Red-eyed Damselfly. However the differences between them are very obvious once one has got one's eye in – and a telescope out! Apart from being much smaller, and having a fluttering flight, the diagnostic difference is that segment 8 of the male's abdomen (i.e. above the blue 'tail') has two distinct blue marks at the sides, narrowing the black area. The eyes of the female are green, rather than brownish red as in the Red-eyed. Although still with a very limited range, it may be gaining a foothold and dispersing to other parts of the county.

Pond with floating ▶
algal mats, Icklesham

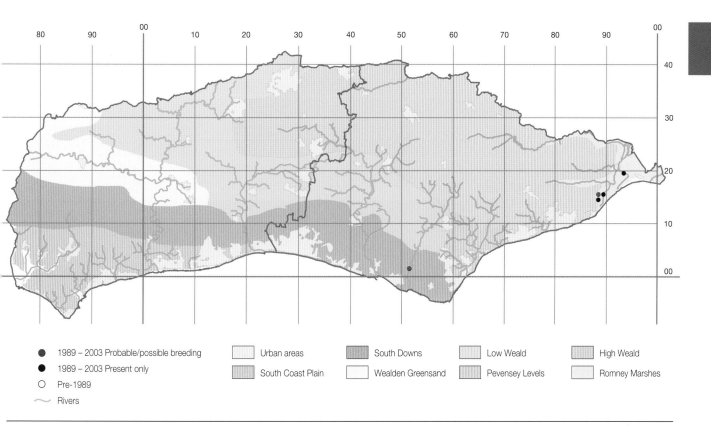

- ● 1989 – 2003 Probable/possible breeding
- ● 1989 – 2003 Present only
- ○ Pre-1989
- ～ Rivers

- ☐ Urban areas
- ☐ South Coast Plain

- ☐ South Downs
- ☐ Wealden Greensand

- ☐ Low Weald
- ☐ Pevensey Levels

- ☐ High Weald
- ☐ Romney Marshes

National status
Our newest species, changed in status from migrant to resident with the first breeding record as recently as 1999, in Essex (Dewick and Gerussi 2000).

Status in Sussex
The first (but still unconfirmed) sighting was at Pett Levels in 2000; the first confirmed one was by F. Lemoine on 10 August 2002 at Icklesham, with subsequent numbers building up to a maximum of 125 on 19 August (Hunter 2003), and with many pairs copulating and ovipositing. In 2003 an additional colony was discovered in the Cuckmere Valley by J. Luck (some 20 pairs).

Habitat
Mainly lakes and ponds with floating vegetation, but the males tend to stay even further away from the banks than the Red-eyed Damselfly. This is true in France where this species is very common but very rarely seen near banks (D. Chelmick, pers. comm.). There is also a preference for submerged vegetation where it breaks the water's surface.

Flight times
Mid June – early September.

Historical records
The first British record followed a dramatic expansion of its range in Europe in the last 30 years.

Conservation
As a species rapidly expanding its range, the Small Red-eyed Damselfly may not yet demand any particular conservation efforts. For now, it is worth monitoring its current sites to note any habitat preferences, and to survey other sites being colonised.

▲ Male

Azure Damselfly
Coenagrion puella

Female ▶

▲ Mating

One of our commonest species, most likely to be found in garden ponds and other small, sheltered water habitats, especially those with plentiful aquatic vegetation. The gaps in distribution in parts of Sussex probably reflect a lack of recording rather than an absence of the Azure Damselfly!

The male is a pale sky-blue with black markings. There is also a distinguishing U shape on the second segment of the abdomen. Females occur in two forms – one (90% of females) is dark with greenish markings on the thorax and abdomen, the other is blue.

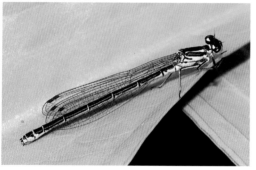

◀ Male

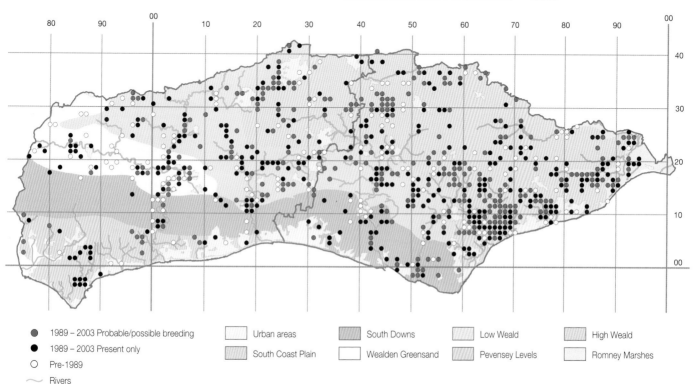

- ● 1989 – 2003 Probable/possible breeding
- ● 1989 – 2003 Present only
- ○ Pre-1989
- ～ Rivers

Urban areas

South Coast Plain

South Downs

Wealden Greensand

Low Weald

Pevensey Levels

High Weald

Romney Marshes

National status
Very common throughout Britain except the northern half of Scotland.

Status in Sussex
The most commonly recorded species in this survey (3759 records). Very well distributed across the whole of the county.

Flight times
Mid May – early September.

Habitat
A wide range such as garden ponds, lakes, streams, rivers, ditches and farm ponds. Sheltered, smaller sites are preferred, with a good range of emergent and marginal vegetation.

Historical records
All historical data appear to match present day findings concerning the widespread distribution of this species. Chelmick noted that it was "generally the most common blue damselfly in base or neutral waters" which is borne out in many of the records from the current survey. However, the size of water body is probably an influencing factor (larger lakes favouring the Common Blue Damselfly) and at some sites, for example at Pevensey Levels, the Azure is less common than the Variable Damselfly.

Conservation
Over-zealous clearance of pond plants could threaten local populations, as would cutting down of marginal vegetation if this significantly reduced shelter. This species is a ready coloniser of new garden ponds.

Variable Damselfly
Coenagrion pulchellum

At first glance this very variable species is easily confused with our other two bright blue damselflies (the Azure and Common Blue). However, its limited range means this is the least likely to be seen. The 'exclamation mark' stripes along the thorax and the 'wine glass' marking at the start of the abdomen in the male

Variable are a help, as is the darker blue when observed with the other species. The female has two forms: one is similar to the male, but with a richer blue; the other is dark, with greenish-yellow markings on the sides.

National status
Scattered and uncommon in mainland Britain, with greatest concentrations in parts of the south and east. In these areas, however, given the right habitat, it can occur in large numbers.

Status in Sussex
Scarce, apart from on the Pevensey Levels, and, to a lesser extent, Amberley Wildbrooks. However, the scattering of occasional records across the county suggests that this species may be under-recorded; if in doubt, recorders may have opted to exclude it from their

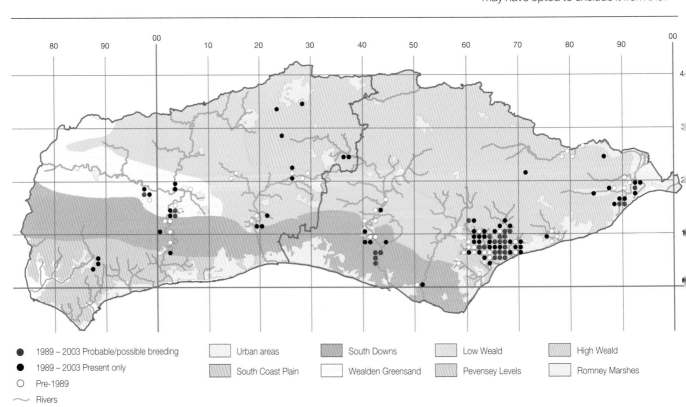

● 1989 – 2003 Probable/possible breeding	Urban areas	South Downs	Low Weald	High Weald
● 1989 – 2003 Present only	South Coast Plain	Wealden Greensand	Pevensey Levels	Romney Marshes
○ Pre-1989			
～ Rivers			

◄ Amberley Wildbrooks

list of sightings, as it is the rarest of the blue damselflies and is listed in the *Sussex Rare Species Inventory*.

Habitat
Fens, water meadows, marshes and shallow ponds; also slow-moving water as in dykes and canals. At Pond Lye near Burgess Hill and Ashburnham Park near Burwash found at the edge of shallow lakes with a very dense and wide emergent vegetation margin dominated by iris and reedmace (D. Chelmick pers. comm.).

Flight times
Mid May – early August.

Historical records
W. Unwin is quoted by Lucas and Bloomfield (1905) and others as having recorded this species near the Winterbourne and elsewhere near Lewes. N. Moore reported it to be a plentiful species in the Ouse Valley north of Lewes in 1945, but it was not recorded in the 1965–1978 survey (Chelmick 1979) or in this one, although both highlight its presence in the Ouse Brooks south of Lewes. Dannreuther (1945) listed this species as "unrecorded in West Sussex". Surprisingly, what is now regarded as its West Sussex stronghold at Amberley Wildbrooks was not discovered until F. Penfold found two there in 1962 (Chelmick 1979).

Conservation
Its favoured habitat in Sussex is traditionally managed grazing pasture and associated ditches, where the water level is high and there is a good range of aquatic and marginal plants. The key practical conservation measure is sympathetic rotational ditch management, but lobbying for more sustainable agriculture practices is critical at policy level.

Mating ▶

Male ▶

◄ Immature male

Common Blue Damselfly
Enallagma cyathigerum

With the Azure, this is our other very common blue damselfly. Where the Azure favours smaller, more sheltered ponds, the Common Blue prefers larger bodies of water. However, they can occur in the same habitat, so close checking of the salient markings is essential. The mushroom- or oval-shaped black mark at the start of the abdomen in the male is clearly distinguishable from the U-shaped marking of the Azure – once you've got your eye in. The female is mainly black, marked over green or blue. Both sexes have large blue eye spots, joined by a bar.

National status
Abundant throughout mainland and offshore Britain.

Status in Sussex
Common, although more surveying is still needed to clarify its exact distribution. It is questionable, for example, whether the epithet 'Common' might have encouraged observers to name too many blue damselflies as this species. On the other hand, has it been under-recorded given the number of gaps still apparent in the maps?

Habitat

Large open waters but also ponds, rivers and slow-flowing streams. Chelmick (1979) stated it favours more acidic sites, but our survey notes a wide distribution across the non-acid landscapes of the Low Weald clay and the Coastal Plain.

Flight times

Mid May – late September.

Historical records

Lucas and Bloomfield (1905) described this species as scarce in Sussex, and reported W. Unwin's statement that it was rare in the Brighton district. Craven (1922) reported finding it near Polegate in 1915, and that at that time there were only two other known sites, at Brighton and Liphook. Dannreuther (1939) described it as "generally distributed" in East Sussex and added (Dannreuther 1945) that "in 1941–42, it was common and seen ovipositing at Hastings". He mentioned (1945) that the "only certain West Sussex record is of 2 males at Lynchmere in September 1923". By contrast (Chelmick 1979) regarded it as "widespread and common", an observation strengthened by our own survey.

Conservation

As its name implies, this is a far from threatened species. However, its preference for large open water habitats makes it vulnerable to neglect if vegetation growth goes unchecked. The positive management of large lakes in our country estates is invaluable in this respect. New water bodies, as an after-use of gravel-pit workings for example, provide the opportunity to create new suitable habitat.

▼ Male

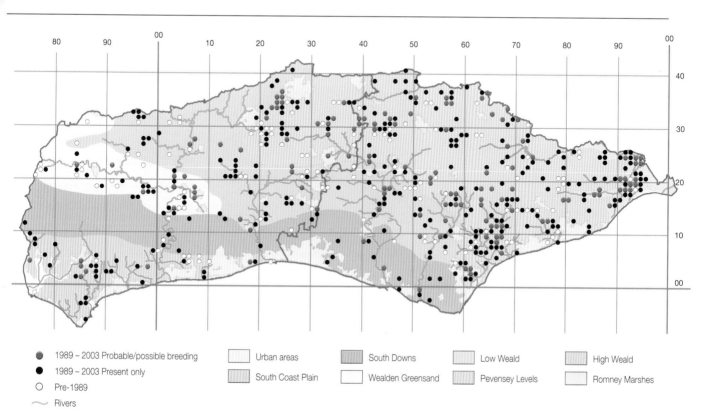

- ● 1989 – 2003 Probable/possible breeding
- ● 1989 – 2003 Present only
- ○ Pre-1989
- ～ Rivers

- ☐ Urban areas
- ☐ South Coast Plain

- ☐ South Downs
- ☐ Wealden Greensand

- ☐ Low Weald
- ☐ Pevensey Levels

- ☐ High Weald
- ☐ Romney Marshes

Blue-tailed Damselfly
Ischnura elegans

▼ A garden pond

Female form 'violacea' ▶

This is one of our most common and widespread species, found in a variety of habitats, including brackish water, and tolerant of mild pollution. The male is a dark blue-black, with a distinctive blue 'tail'. The female has a number of forms, including one like the male.

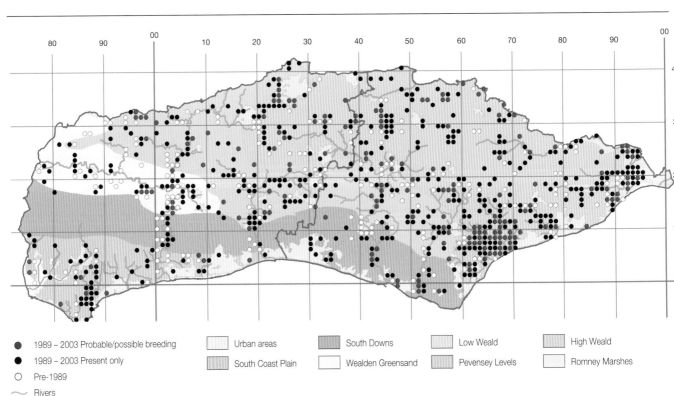

- ● 1989 – 2003 Probable/possible breeding
- ● 1989 – 2003 Present only
- ○ Pre-1989
- ～ Rivers

- Urban areas
- South Coast Plain
- South Downs
- Wealden Greensand
- Low Weald
- Pevensey Levels
- High Weald
- Romney Marshes

◀ Female form 'rufescens'

◀ Male (far left)

▼ Freshly emerged insect
with exuvia

National status
Abundant throughout Britain.

Status in Sussex
Common, the number of records (3692) exceeded only by that of the Azure Damselfly. Very well distributed across the whole county, with marked concentrations in the east, and occurring even on the Downs where there is water.

Habitat
A range of still or slow-moving waters, including garden ponds, streams, rivers, canals, ditches and pools. The species tolerates pollution more than other species.

Flight times
Mid May – early September.

Historical records
A widespread species historically (e.g. Dannreuther 1939, 1945). Chelmick (1979) noted its reduced abundance in acid waters such as those on Ashdown Forest.

Conservation
This species, most common in the south of the country, raises no conservation concerns. As an early coloniser of newly created wetland habitat, it is an easy species to encourage – and, in doing so, we can perhaps help other dragonflies to extend their range too.

Small Red Damselfly
Ceriagrion tenellum

Small heathland ▶
pool, Ashdown
Forest

This national rarity is confined in Sussex to small, acid heathland bogs, mainly on Ashdown Forest. Small, delicate and weak-flying, it is hard to spot as it hovers over mats of *Sphagnum* moss. Except for a blackish thorax, the male is almost entirely red, including the legs. The female occurs in three forms, the most common resembling the male.

Male ▶

National status
Rare, restricted to southern England and west Wales.

Status in Sussex
Overall rare (with only 95 post 1989 records). Centred on Ashdown Forest but also near Liphook, West Chiltington and south east of Tunbridge Wells. Listed in the *Sussex Rare Species Inventory*.

Habitat
Only heathland bogs and pools, usually edged with *Sphagnum* moss.

Flight times
Early June – September.

Historical records
First recorded in Sussex near Liphook at the end of the nineteenth century, it was still there during the mid 1970s (Chelmick 1979). A specimen was taken by H. Guermonprez at West Chiltington on 11 September 1917 (Dannreuther 1945). There were no sightings in what is thought to be the same area during the 1970s and 1980s, but the species was 'rediscovered' there in 1990, and re-emerged after several very dry years in 1995 (Chelmick 1997). Stated as "abundant" in the Tunbridge Wells and Crowborough areas in 1908, it was not found there between 1932 and 1938, although N. Moore recorded "many *in coitu*" on 9 August 1947 (HESN 1948) in the Crowborough area. At one site in that area, where it was recorded in 1947, only one individual was recorded in 1991. There is a report of four near Beckley by J. Ashbee on 18 May 1974 (HESN 1975) which Chelmick (1979) suggested were vagrants. However, the group of recent records in Ashdown Forest had very little historical background before Chelmick (1979). Fowles (1985) found the Small Red "on a series of small boggy pools in the Chelwood Gate area". Marrable (1999) reported its loss from two of Fowles's sites and its arrival at a new pond prepared for it. Since then it has also colonised a further pool a kilometre away from these others. Within the

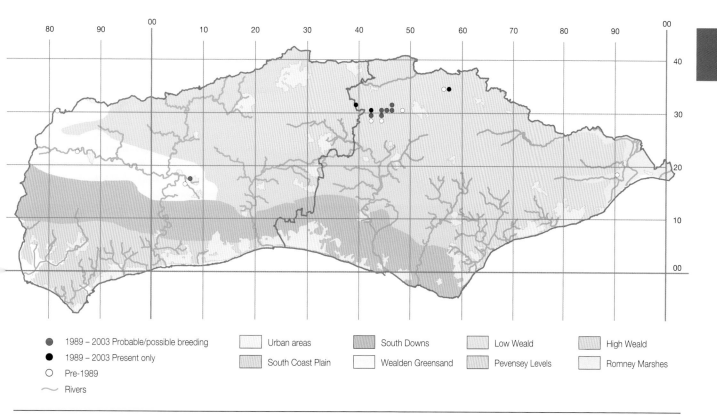

- ● 1989 – 2003 Probable/possible breeding
- ● 1989 – 2003 Present only
- ○ Pre-1989
- ～ Rivers

☐ Urban areas	▨ South Downs
▨ South Coast Plain	☐ Wealden Greensand

▨ Low Weald	▨ High Weald
▨ Pevensey Levels	☐ Romney Marshes

▲ Female form 'melanogastrum'

Female form ▶ 'typica'

ancient Pale of Ashdown Forest the species is also present at the Sussex Wildlife Trust Old Lodge reserve (on four ponds in 2003) and in the Pippingford Ministry of Defence training area.

Conservation

Chelmick (1979) feared that, without conservation action, the species "will soon be extinct" in Sussex. The clearing of over-shadowing scrub from pool-side edges, and the creation of new ponds near existing populations, are clearly benefiting the species on Ashdown Forest. Recent scrub clearance and wetland creation at Hurston Warren should also benefit the Small Red. While climate change may bring warmer conditions favourable for this Mediterranean species, longer, drier summers could also dry out the pools where it breeds.

Migrant Hawker
Aeshna mixta

Male ▶

▼ Female

This is our smallest hawker (*Aeshna* species), with an abdomen well-marked in blue in the male and dull green in the female. It is most abundant in late summer, when numbers are boosted by migration. It is often seen away from water, for example hawking in the tree-tops in sunny woodland glades.

Male ▶

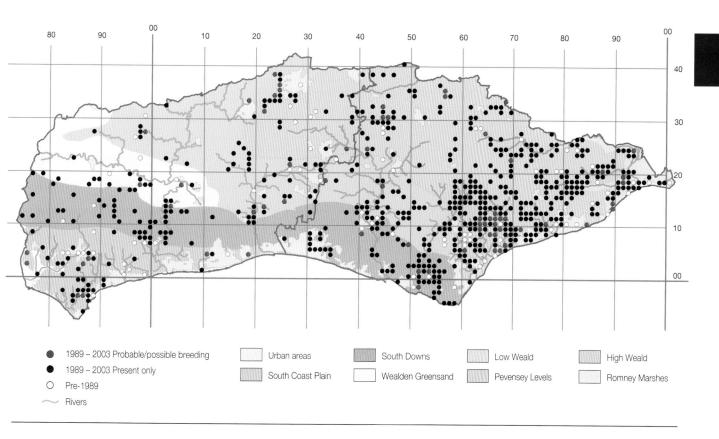

- ● 1989 – 2003 Probable/possible breeding
- ● 1989 – 2003 Present only
- ○ Pre-1989
- ～ Rivers

Urban areas	South Downs
South Coast Plain	Wealden Greensand
Low Weald	High Weald
Pevensey Levels	Romney Marshes

Larva ▶

National status
Strongholds in southern England, common all over the Midlands and extending its range to northern England

Status in Sussex
Occurs throughout the county, but especially in the east, and boosted by immigration in late summer. An exceptional inland record was of 300 recorded at Bewl Water by P. Bance on 11 August 1995.

Habitat
Mainly still waters such as lakes and ponds, even canals, but can occur almost anywhere, for example in woodland and towns and gardens.

Flight times
Late July – late October.

Historical records
Lucas and Bloomfield (1905) first reported this species in East Sussex from two sites that were also mentioned by Craven (1922): Camber Sands (1899) and Guestling (1900). When Craven (1922) caught a specimen at Mountfield on 12 August 1916, it was still considered a rare insect. Dannreuther (1945) listed 25 specimens from the Guermonprez collection, with the earliest from West Sussex dated 1894. Chelmick (1979) found it breeding throughout the county and mentioned "huge numbers" flying in off the sea at Beachy Head in September 1975 and 1976, and populations in coastal localities reaching "spectacular proportions".

Conservation
Climate change may well be a significant factor in this species becoming very common (from being a rare migrant 50 or so years ago) and extending its range north and west. Colonization of reservoirs and former gravel pits highlights the value of creating new water bodies for species such as the Migrant Hawker, which has readily taken to these sites in Sussex.

Southern Hawker
Aeshna cyanea

A large dark brown- or black-bodied hawker with most abdominal spots being green in the male and all of them being yellowish green in the female. Both sexes are distinguished from other *Aeshna* hawkers by segments 9 and 10 of the abdomen having a band – blue in the male, green in the female – rather than paired spots. It is often seen beating along woodland rides and is a regular visitor to garden ponds. The males are strongly territorial and engage in noisy, aerial combat. Both sexes will readily approach observers.

▼ Male

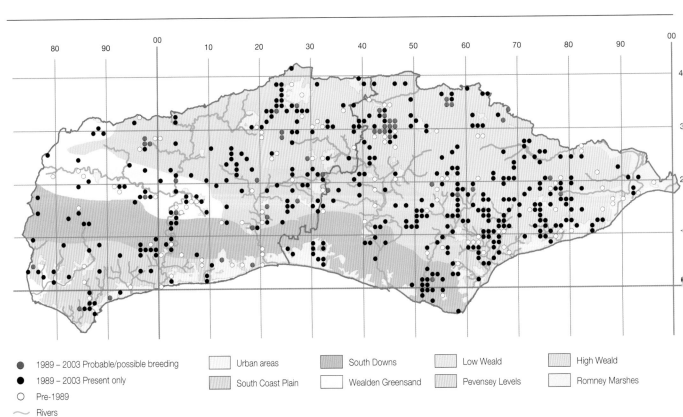

- ● 1989 – 2003 Probable/possible breeding
- ● 1989 – 2003 Present only
- ○ Pre-1989
- ~ Rivers

Urban areas	South Downs
South Coast Plain	Wealden Greensand

Low Weald	High Weald
Pevensey Levels	Romney Marshes

◀ Emergence

▼ Female

▼ Immature female

Historical records

With an extremely catholic taste as regards habitat, it is not surprising that this species has always been well recorded throughout the county. Dannreuther (1939) suggested that its numbers might occasionally be reinforced by immigration from the south. Chelmick (1979) felt that this species was under-recorded. Certainly our survey has added a considerable number of records, resulting in a map showing much greater coverage across the county.

National status

Appropriately named, being very common in southern England and Wales; extending its range northwards.

Status in Sussex

Common all over the county, even away from water.

Habitat

A wide range, such as lakes, ponds, canals, slow-moving streams, ditches and garden ponds.

Flight times

Early July – early October.

Conservation

Although very common, the Southern Hawker still faces the same threats of pollution and habitat destruction as other species. At home in the urban environment, it can benefit from the digging of new garden ponds.

Brown Hawker
Aeshna grandis

Female egg-laying ▶

This is a common and easily identified hawker since both sexes have wings tinged with amber-brown, noticeable even in flight. It has lemon-yellow stripes on the thorax and spots – sky-blue in the male, yellow in the female – down the side of the abdomen.

▼ Male

▲ Female

◀ Lake Wood, Uckfield

◄ Female

National status
Generally common and widespread, though absent from Scotland and some parts of the South West.

Status in Sussex
More common towards the east of the county. Much more local in West Sussex, apart from a strong presence on the Arun. The general distribution pattern does not appear to have changed much over the years.

Habitat
Large and well-vegetated lakes and ponds, occasionally slow-moving water such as canals.

Flight times
Early July – early October.

Historical records
This species appears to have always been more common in East than West Sussex. Interestingly, Dannreuther (1939, 1945) claimed that the first county record was by W. Markwick on 29 July 1802 at Denne Park, Horsham. In 1945 Dannreuther listed only one other site in West Sussex. Chelmick (1979) considered this species the most common *Aeshna* in the High Weald.

Conservation
It readily colonises gravel pits, canals and other sites abandoned by industry and then flooded or created as wetland habitat. It can tolerate the residual pollution of many ex-industrial sites.

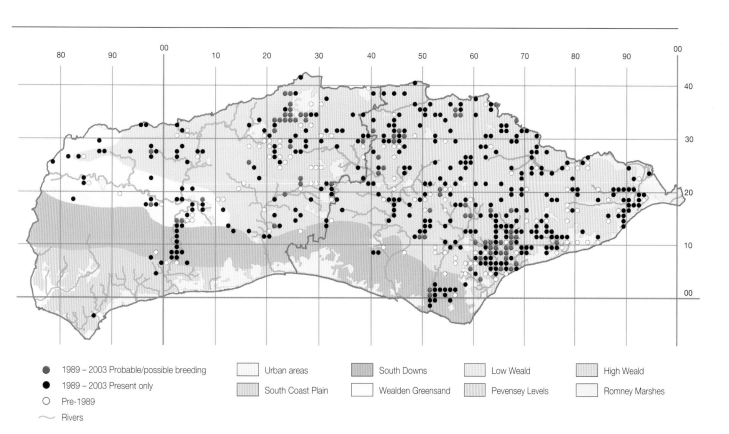

- ● 1989 – 2003 Probable/possible breeding
- ● 1989 – 2003 Present only
- ○ Pre-1989
- ⌇ Rivers

Urban areas	South Downs	Low Weald	High Weald
South Coast Plain	Wealden Greensand	Pevensey Levels	Romney Marshes

Emperor Dragonfly
Anax imperator

The Emperor is our largest dragonfly, with broad wings and a robust body. The male has a green thorax and bright blue abdomen with a black dorsal stripe running the entire length. The female has a mainly green thorax and abdomen. Very aptly named, this species aggressively dominates still-water habitats, from small garden ponds and dew ponds, to large lakes and reservoirs. Aerial 'dog-fights' between rival males are an impressive spectacle.

▼ Old female

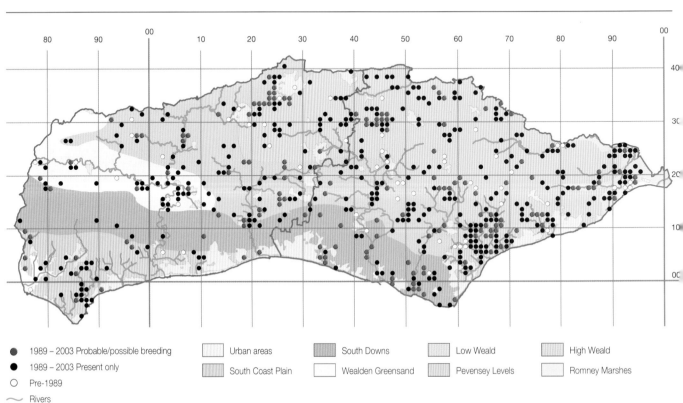

- ● 1989 – 2003 Probable/possible breeding
- ● 1989 – 2003 Present only
- ○ Pre-1989
- ～ Rivers

- Urban areas
- South Coast Plain
- South Downs
- Wealden Greensand
- Low Weald
- Pevensey Levels
- High Weald
- Romney Marshes

◄ Female egg-laying

▼ Larva

▲ Male

National status
Widespread in southern England and southern Wales; extending its range northwards.

Status in Sussex
Common all over the county wherever there is suitable habitat. There are more post 1989 records (2509) than for any other hawker.

Habitat
Still waters like ponds, lakes, gravel pits and canals.

Flight times
Late May – early September.

Historical records
Dannreuther (1939) regarded this as a "rather local southern species" but most other authors have suggested that this has always been a common insect in Sussex. Chelmick (1979) commented that in the south west of the county it was less common than elsewhere, but our survey has provided a number of records for this area.

Conservation
As an early coloniser of new ponds, and perhaps our most magnificent dragonfly, the Emperor provides a great incentive to creating new wetland habitats.

Hairy Dragonfly
Brachytron pratense

Pevensey Levels ▶

This is our earliest dragonfly of the year, appearing from early May onwards. When perched, the hairy thorax, from which it gets its name, is very evident. The thorax in the male is brown with green stripes and the abdomen is black with blue spots. The female is similar, but the blue is replaced by yellow.

▼ Mating

National status
Becoming increasingly common and widespread across England and Wales, but rare in Scotland.

Status in Sussex
Rather localised along the county's river systems and in its coastal wetlands, but slowly expanding its range. Listed in the *Sussex Rare Species Inventory*.

Habitat
Clean, still-water bodies such as lakes, ponds, old gravel pits, canals and ditches with an abundance of vegetation.

Flight times
Early May – early July.

Historical records
According to W. Unwin's account in Merrifield (1860), this species was frequently encountered during his surveying in the 1850s. Lucas and Bloomfield (1905) also listed reports from the Abbots Wood area near Polegate where it still occurs despite significant plantings made by the Forestry Commission. Craven (1922) and Dannreuther (1939) also included other sightings in their reports, but Chelmick's survey results (1979) suggested a decline along the coastal levels and river valleys in the far east of the county. More sympathetic farming practices over recent years probably account for the steady improvement in this dragonfly's status.

Conservation
This species has been badly affected by intensive farming since World War Two. More recently, however, it has benefited from schemes such as Countryside Stewardship that have encouraged more traditional land management and helped protect wetland habitats like grazing meadows and associated ditches. At Amberley Wildbrooks this species thrives only in areas where the typical grazing regime continues. The cattle poach the edges of the dykes and maintain open habitats for the males to patrol. The high banks from the excavated dykes provide shelter for flying during windy conditions. In areas of the Brooks where grazing has ceased, the Hairy Dragonfly no longer occurs. Consistently warmer springs are leading to the earlier emergence of nymphs.

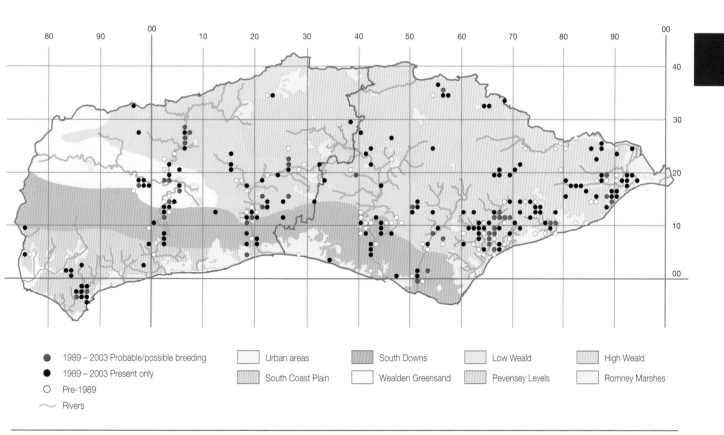

● 1989 – 2003 Probable/possible breeding
● 1989 – 2003 Present only
○ Pre-1989
〜 Rivers

☐ Urban areas
☐ South Coast Plain
☐ South Downs
☐ Wealden Greensand
☐ Low Weald
☐ Pevensey Levels
☐ High Weald
☐ Romney Marshes

▲ Male

◀ Female

Male ▶

Club-tailed Dragonfly
Gomphus vulgatissimus

Immature male ▷

This is a very special dragonfly for Sussex, with a nationally important population on the River Arun. It is a medium sized hawker, with a distinctive club shaped 'tail'. Both sexes are black with contrasting yellow and green markings.

River Rother near Fittleworth ▷

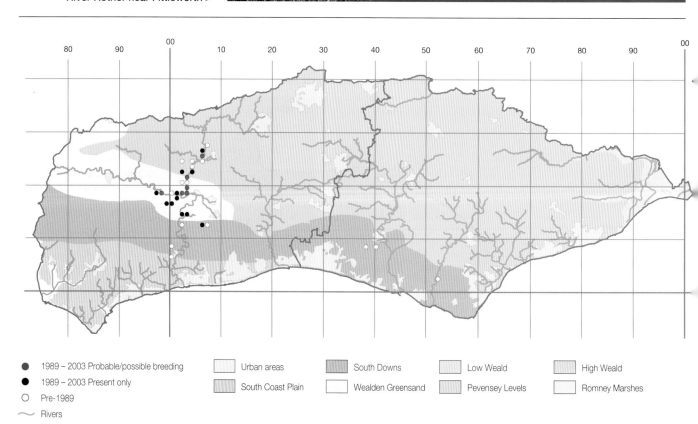

● 1989 – 2003 Probable/possible breeding

● 1989 – 2003 Present only

○ Pre-1989

～ Rivers

Urban areas

South Coast Plain

South Downs

Wealden Greensand

Low Weald

Pevensey Levels

High Weald

Romney Marshes

46

◀ Old male

▲ Female

National status

Very local, confined to seven river systems in southern England and Wales.

Status in Sussex

Confined to the River Arun and adjacent Rother in West Sussex. Listed in the *Sussex Rare Species Inventory*.

Habitat

Moderate to slow-flowing rivers with a muddy or silty bottom; often uses mid-stream perches.

Flight times

Mid May – early July.

Historical records

Lucas and Bloomfield (1905) and some later authors reported single specimens taken by W. Unwin on the Lewes Downs in 1846 and in Love Lane, Lewes in 1851. Although Dannreuther (1939) described them as "rare wanderers", there is nonetheless the possibility that this species once occurred on the Ouse. It was also reported on the Cuckmere river in the 1930s, but was not found there during the 1965–1978 survey (Chelmick 1979). It was first recorded at its present stronghold on the Arun in 1912 (Chelmick 1979). It would appear to be restricted to limited stretches of the river as the current distribution pattern now is very similar to that shown by Chelmick (1979).

Conservation

Why this species is now restricted in Sussex to the River Arun is not known. Its vulnerability was highlighted in early 2003 when an agricultural pesticide polluted the river near Billingshurst and wiped out the dragonfly fauna and other aquatic life.

Golden-ringed Dragonfly
Cordulegaster boltonii

Mating ▶

Thanks to its long ovipositor, the female is actually our longest dragonfly (84mm, 3½ inches), though it is much slimmer than the Emperor. Perhaps because of its superficial likeness to a giant wasp, this species gave rise to the old folk name for a dragonfly – horse-stinger! On the black abdomen the yellow markings look like rings.

Female ▶

▼ **Heathland stream, Ashdown Forest**

National status
Common in southern England, Wales, the Lake District and western Scotland.

Status in Sussex
Scarce. Mostly confined to Wealden Greensand and across the High Weald, most prominently on Ashdown Forest.

Habitat
Lake outfalls and moderate to fast flowing streams with a gravel or silt bottom. May feed in woodland, as long as there are some clear, open areas.

Flight times
Mid June – early September.

Historical records
Unwin (1853) appears to have been the first to record this species, in 1853 in the Brighton area. Furley (1931) reported that it was seen most years in July at Arundel. In the supposedly more suitable habitat of Ashdown Forest, it was not recorded until the 1920s (Chelmick 1979). Elsewhere in Sussex, records have always been somewhat localised. There were no records from the Wealden Greensand from the 1965–1978 survey (Chelmick 1979).

Conservation
This species depends on the presence of open heathland. Removing coniferous plantations (and their shade) could help extend the number of sites it frequents.

◀ Male

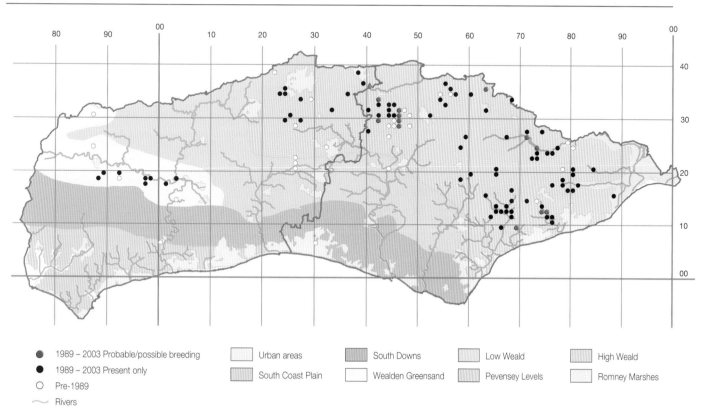

- ● 1989 – 2003 Probable/possible breeding
- ● 1989 – 2003 Present only
- ○ Pre-1989
- ∼ Rivers

| | Urban areas | | South Downs | | Low Weald | | High Weald |
| | South Coast Plain | | Wealden Greensand | | Pevensey Levels | | Romney Marshes |

Downy Emerald
Cordulia aenea

The two emerald dragonfly species can be found at the same site, patrolling fairly sheltered heathland ponds or hawking high in the woodland canopy, rarely settling. As a result, distinguishing between them can be a frustrating task. The Downy Emerald usually goes for the more open areas, flying very low, regularly turning back and forth, and hovering. It appears shiny black in flight, except for the transparent wings. Both sexes have a bronze-green downy thorax and a dark metallic green abdomen, which is club-shaped in the male and rounded in the female. Young newly breeding adults have beautiful greenish yellow eyes and bronzy abdomens going duller with age. The female lacks the conspicuous ovipositor (vulvar scale) of the Brilliant Emerald.

▲ Mating

Male ▶

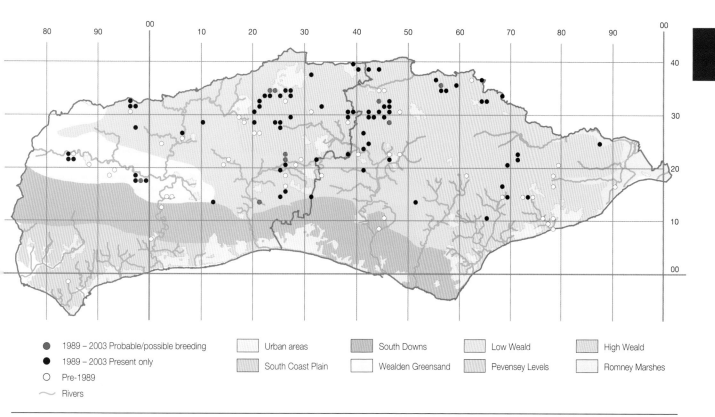

▲ Male hovering

National status

A nationally rare species, and listed in the *British Red Data Book on Invertebrates*. With a stronghold in south-east England, it has an otherwise scattered distribution from Devon to the Scottish Highlands.

Status in Sussex

Thinly but widely scattered across the county, including the south-east, from where the 1965–1978 survey had no breeding records (Chelmick 1979). Listed in the *Sussex Rare Species Inventory*.

Habitat

Preference for nutrient-poor, acidic, tree-lined or woodland (usually deciduous) ponds, lakes and canals. Occasionally, slow-flowing rivers and streams, with trees and overhanging branches.

Flight times

Mid May – late July.

Historical records

All authorities (e.g. Lucas and Bloomfield 1905; Craven 1922) seem to agree that the first record for Sussex is by W. Unwin who found one near Horsham in June 1846. However, up until 1945 there had been only three localities recorded in West Sussex (Dannreuther 1945), and it seems to have fared only slightly better in East Sussex (Chelmick 1979). In the north and west of the county Chelmick (1979) considered it widespread and common.

Conservation

Since the larvae live in the slowly decomposing vegetation at the bottom of (usually still) waterbodies, dredging could pose a serious threat. A further threat comes from nutrient enrichment of water caused by run-off from adjacent cultivated land or fertilised pasture. Loss of woodland ponds or clearance of their tree-lined fringes poses problems for the adults.

Brilliant Emerald
Somatochlora metallica

This national rarity differs from the Downy Emerald in a few subtle respects. It is larger and looks a brighter green in flight. It flies faster and more purposefully, with less turning and pausing, and tends to stick close to the trees and in the shade. Close examination is needed to separate the two species, though the female Brilliant has an obvious spike (vulvar scale) on its underside near the end of its abdomen.

▼ Lake on Ashdown Forest

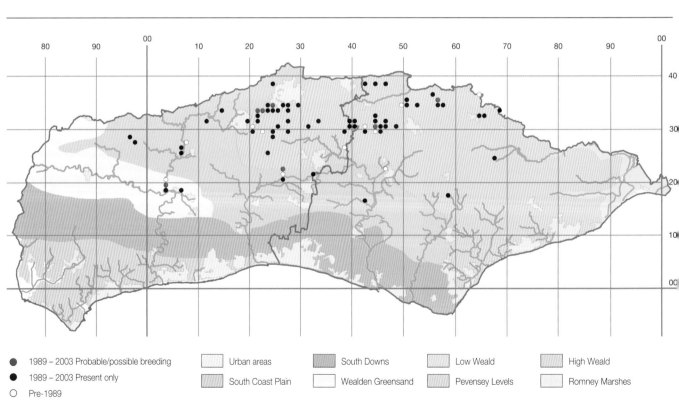

● 1989 – 2003 Probable/possible breeding

● 1989 – 2003 Present only

○ Pre-1989

〜 Rivers

Urban areas	South Downs
South Coast Plain	Wealden Greensand

Low Weald   High Weald

Pevensey Levels   Romney Marshes

◀ Male
▼ Male

National status
Rare. Two widely separated and disjunct populations, south-east England and the Scottish Highlands. Some of the most significant southern populations occur in Sussex.

Status in Sussex
Locally common. Concentrated on the northern woodland ridges of the High Weald, with a few outliers in the upper Arun and Adur river catchments. Listed in the *Sussex Rare Species Inventory*.

Habitat
Similar to that of the Downy Emerald: mildly acidic, usually large, still, relatively vegetation-free waterbodies, often set in pine woodland with sheltered bays and overhanging trees and bushes.

Flight times
Early June – late August.

Historical records
According to Bloomfield (1910), the finding of this species by E. Speyer at a site near Tunbridge Wells in August 1908 was the first record for Sussex. However, Dannreuther (1939) listed an earlier record by W. Lucas in 1900, at Crowborough. By the time of the 1965–1978 survey, and within its habitat constraints, it appears to have become relatively common (Chelmick 1979).

Conservation
Maintaining large ponds and lakes in the northern heathy belt of the county will help this species. Its larvae live in the detritus of dead leaves, twigs and other vegetation. To improve many larger ponds for fishing, dredging and the removal of bankside cover are often carried out, so raising awareness of the consequences among anglers is important.

Four-spotted Chaser
Libellula quadrimaculata

▼ Male

This common, tawny to dark brown species is easy to identify. All four wings have a dark mark at the node, from which the species derives its name, and the hindwings in particular have a conspicuous dark patch at their base. Both the male and female have a predominantly brown thorax and abdomen, the tip of which is black. Fine hairs cover the thorax. The male is highly territorial.

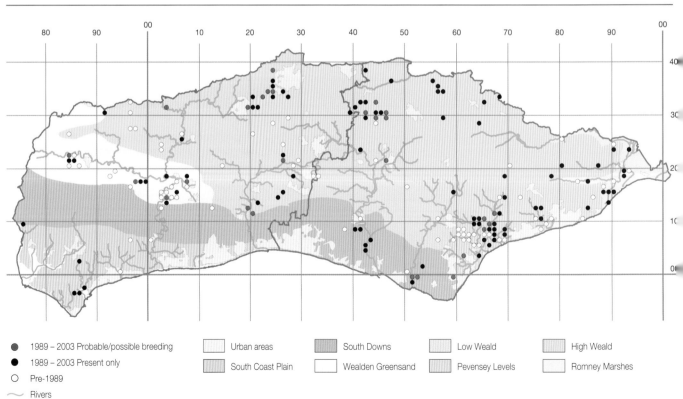

● 1989 – 2003 Probable/possible breeding
● 1989 – 2003 Present only
○ Pre-1989
〰 Rivers

	Urban areas		South Downs		Low Weald		High Weald
	South Coast Plain		Wealden Greensand		Pevensey Levels		Romney Marshes

◀ Male form
'praenubila'

National status
Common throughout Britain.

Status in Sussex
Patchily distributed and locally common across the county, especially on Wealden Greensand, in High Weald localities such as Ashdown Forest, and on Pevensey Levels.

Habitat
A wide range of mainly still, acid waters, from bog pools on heathland, to pits and ponds. Occasionally found on slow-flowing streams.

Flight times
Late May – mid August.

Historical records
Dannreuther (1941) made no mention of Sussex in his "Preliminary note on dragonfly migration" in which he described the well recorded migration of this species across Europe, including landfalls of thousands of insects in Kent (see also Parr 1996). Although locally abundant in its favoured habitats, the 1965–1978 survey map displayed many gaps across the county (Chelmick 1979), which are still present, but smaller, in our current survey.

Conservation
More needs to be discovered about the particular requirements of this species, as it has a patchy distribution in the county, found in some sites of a characteristic habitat, but absent from others. As with other acid pool dwellers, maintaining open heath and associated water-bodies, preventing scrub invasion and creating new ponds will all benefit this species.

Scarce Chaser
Libellula fulva

Adult male ▶

The Scarce Chaser occurs on just a few river systems in England so the Sussex population is important. Among British species, the male has a unique combination of a black-tipped, powder-blue abdomen, and dark patches at the base of the wings. The maturing female has a velvety ginger appearance, with a distinct smoky patch at the tip of each wing and a saffron streak along their upper edge. As it ages it goes a drab brown.

National status
Restricted to about ten river systems and nearby still waters in southern and eastern England. Populations appear to be stable and there is some evidence that the species may be extending its range. Listed in the *British Red Data Book on Invertebrates*.

Status in Sussex
Confined to West Sussex, although there have been very occasional sightings in East Sussex. Its range is largely confined to the River Arun, from Billingshurst to Amberley, where it can occur in large numbers. There are a few records for the western Rother, where it meets the Arun and a few sporadic sightings on the Adur tributaries. Listed in the *Sussex Rare Species Inventory*.

Habitat
Slow-moving rivers with water meadows, occasionally gravel pits and ponds. It has a preference for sunny, sheltered spots, with plenty of vegetation, avoiding areas of heavy shade.

▲ Adult female

Immature male ▶

◄ View from Stopham bridge, River Arun

Flight times
Mid May – mid July.

Historical records
According to Lucas and Bloomfield (1905) and later authors the first record seems to have been by W. Unwin on the Lewes Downs and reported by him in *The Naturalist* of July 1853. Although observed by G. Furley at Midhurst in 1924, it was not until 1937 that J. Cowley recorded it at its present stronghold on the Arun (Chelmick 1979).

Conservation
Throughout its British range the Scarce Chaser is vulnerable to river pollution, and land drainage and reclamation schemes. Concern about the species is not new: Longfield (1937) wrote that "it should be very carefully preserved where it does breed". Recent decades have seen a significant conversion from traditional wet grazing meadows to drained arable fields, in Sussex as elsewhere. This change of habitat, alongside pollution from fertilisers and pesticides, has adversely affected the Scarce Chaser, even though the River Arun itself is nominally protected by its status as a Site of Special Scientific Interest. We need to improve our understanding of the species' ecological requirements.

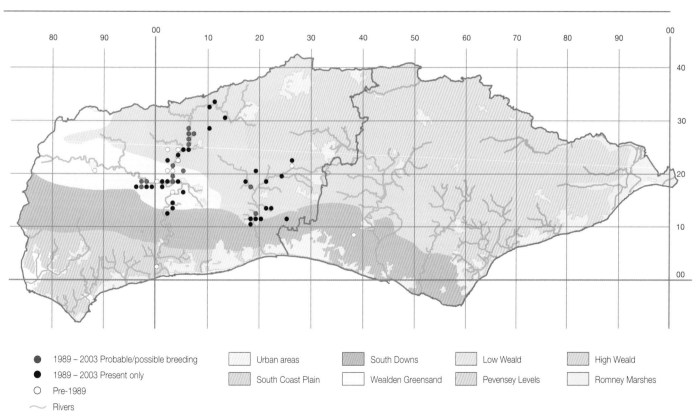

- ● 1989 – 2003 Probable/possible breeding
- ● 1989 – 2003 Present only
- ○ Pre-1989
- ∼ Rivers

Urban areas	South Downs
South Coast Plain	Wealden Greensand

Low Weald | High Weald
Pevensey Levels | Romney Marshes

Broad-bodied Chaser
Libellula depressa

This is a very common dragonfly, obliging too, as it often returns to the same perch to look out for prey or mark its territory. An early coloniser of new ponds and a garden favourite, it is easily identified with its broad, blue (male) or golden-brown (female) abdomen. Both sexes have dark patches at the base of each wing. The immature male initially looks like the female.

National status
Widespread and common throughout southern and central England and Wales, rarer in the Midlands and absent in the North.

Status in Sussex
Common. Well distributed over the whole of the county, even in urban areas and across the South Downs.

Habitat
A wide variety of still waters, including garden ponds, lakes, canals and ditches, sometimes slow-moving rivers, but rarely those with acid waters; also open waters, with some aquatic and marginal plants.

Flight times
Mid May – early August.

Historical records
Although Dannreuther (1939) said of this species that it was "a resident sometimes common due to immigration from the Continent, established as resident in places", all other authors have treated it as common and widespread.

Conservation
Clearance of dense aquatic growth is desirable but, as the larvae live in the mud at the bottom of a pond or other suitable water habitat, it needs to be sensitively carried out. Maintaining open bank-sides is also desirable for the adults. As a classic early coloniser, it readily takes to newly created garden ponds.

▼ Pond near Henfield

◄ Immature male

▼ Male

▼ Freshly emerged female with exuvia

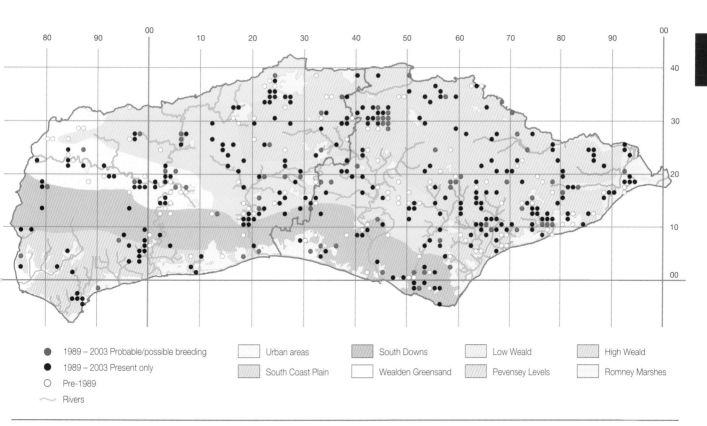

● 1989 – 2003 Probable/possible breeding
● 1989 – 2003 Present only
○ Pre-1989
~ Rivers

☐ Urban areas
▨ South Coast Plain
▨ South Downs
☐ Wealden Greensand
▨ Low Weald
▨ Pevensey Levels
▨ High Weald
☐ Romney Marshes

◀ Female

Black-tailed Skimmer
Orthetrum cancellatum

Immature male ▶

The skimmers are similar to the chasers, but less broad in the abdomen and with completely clear wings. This species prefers still water and has undoubtedly extended its range thanks to the increase in the number of flooded gravel pits. It is a fast, low-flying insect but, between bursts of activity defending territory or catching food, spends time resting on a regular perch, usually a stick or bare ground. The male has a grey-brown thorax and a powder-blue abdomen with a black tip and yellow-orange, elongated spots on the sides. The female (and immature male) is yellowish-brown with black, curved bracket-shaped markings on either side of the abdomen. There are some pronounced changes with age, the male often bearing black scratch marks where the female's legs have grasped the abdomen during mating and the female turning to a tawny-brown or bluish-grey colour.

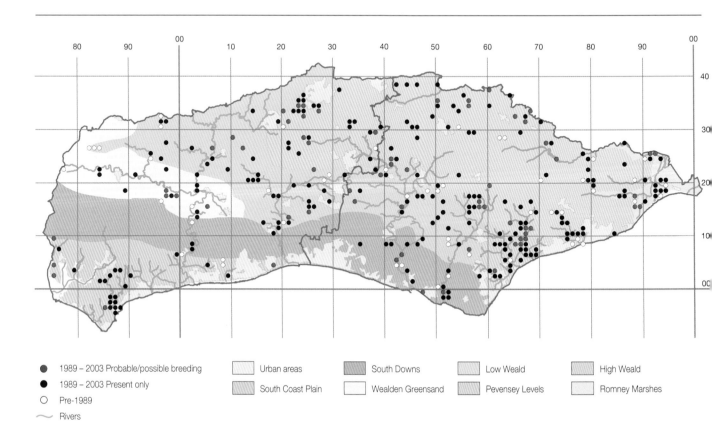

- ● 1989 – 2003 Probable/possible breeding
- ● 1989 – 2003 Present only
- ○ Pre-1989
- ～ Rivers

- Urban areas
- South Coast Plain
- South Downs
- Wealden Greensand
- Low Weald
- Pevensey Levels
- High Weald
- Romney Marshes

▲ Male

◄ Flooded gravel pit near Chichester

Immature male ▶

National status
Fairly common in southern England and parts of Wales. Extending its range significantly northwards into the Midlands and beyond.

Status in Sussex
Locally common across the whole of the county. Possibly under-recorded as there are a number of suitable sites where it has not been recorded, exemplified by the patchy distribution across the Low Weald.

Flight times
Late May – early August.

Habitat
Large, shallow open ponds, lakes, gravel pits and occasionally slow-moving rivers, adjacent ditches and small ponds. Liking for bare ground at the waterside where the males can sun themselves.

Historical records
Despite its now reasonable county-wide distribution, this species was barely recorded in East Sussex until 1935 (Dannreuther 1939). Although Chelmick (1979) stated that it was not recorded from West Sussex before the 1965 –1978 survey, there does appear to have been a pre-1900 record from near Liphook, reported by Lucas (1900). As in our survey, Chelmick (1979) considered it to be widespread but local over the county.

Conservation
The conversion of exhausted gravel pits into lakes has been a conservation success in terms of expansion in the range of this species. It is important to ensure these sites are well managed and not neglected to scrub over.

Keeled Skimmer
Orthetrum coerulescens

In Sussex this species is at the extreme eastern edge of its range, occurring at a few heathland pools. It is a darter-sized dragonfly, with a slim tapering abdomen. The all-blue abdomen of the mature male has a pronounced 'keel', especially when viewed from the side. The female has a golden-brown abdomen, which darkens with age, with a thin black stripe along the top.

National status
Locally common, with a patchy distribution mainly in western Britain.

Status in Sussex
Rare, with only 12 pre-1989 and 39 post-1989 records, most of them on Ashdown Forest, our only relatively secure locality. Listed in the *Sussex Rare Species Inventory*.

Habitat
Acid pools, streams and ditches in wet heath areas, usually where *Sphagnum* moss is present.

Flight times
Late June – early August.

Historical records
The third species first recorded in Sussex near Tunbridge Wells in August 1908 by E. Speyer (Bloomfield 1910), it was also found at Amberley Wildbrooks by H. Guermonprez on 10 August 1909 (Dannreuther 1945). Chelmick (1979) wrote that "This rare species, with the exception of *Lestes dryas*, has declined more than any other in recent years" and that there was just one locality for it at the time (east of Crowborough). On

▲ Male

Female ▶

◀ Boggy pool on Ashdown Forest   Mating ▼

Ashdown Forest Fowles (1985) did not record it, but Marrable (1999) found it at two sites, and this survey did in six 1x1 kilometre squares in the county as a whole.

Conservation

The conservation, restoration or creation of small bog ponds on our wet heaths, a priority habitat, could help expand the range and number of sites for this species.

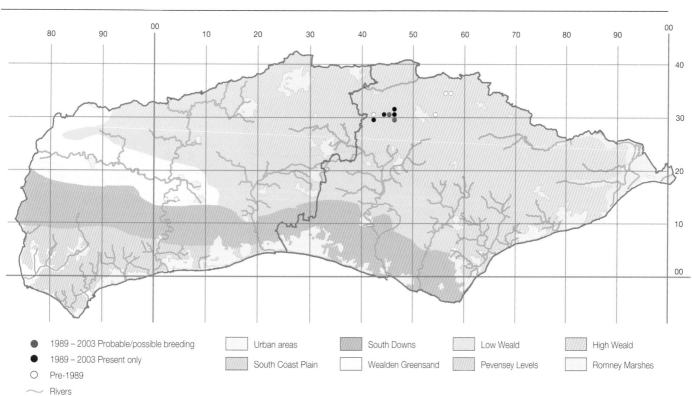

● 1989 – 2003 Probable/possible breeding

● 1989 – 2003 Present only

○ Pre-1989

〜 Rivers

Urban areas	South Downs
South Coast Plain	Wealden Greensand

Low Weald · High Weald · Pevensey Levels · Romney Marshes

Common Darter
Sympetrum striolatum

Woodland ride, ▶
Selhurst Park, near
East Dean,
Chichester

This is one of our most common and easily spotted dragonflies. It is a robust species, surviving into October or even November in dry, sunny and mild autumns. The male has a parallel-sided, orange-red abdomen and a brown thorax. The female is dull yellow-brown on both the abdomen and thorax.

▼ Old female

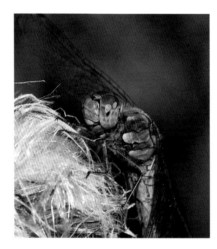

National status

Abundant in England and Wales, less common in Scotland.

Status in Sussex

Common. Very well distributed over the whole of the county, especially in the east. Its 268 pre 1989 and 2397 post 1989 records exceed the figures for any other Anisopteran. The offshore record is not a misprint. It represents a Common Darter seen on 16 June 1958 by S. Sharman on the Royal Sovereign Light Vessel!

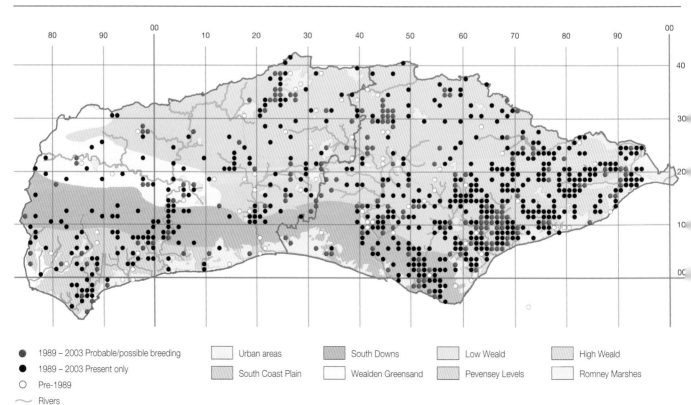

- ● 1989 – 2003 Probable/possible breeding
- ● 1989 – 2003 Present only
- ○ Pre-1989
- 〜 Rivers

- ☐ Urban areas
- ☐ South Coast Plain

- ☐ South Downs
- ☐ Wealden Greensand

- ☐ Low Weald
- ☐ Pevensey Levels

- ☐ High Weald
- ☐ Romney Marshes

Female ▶

▼ Male

◀ Male

Habitat
All forms of water, including ponds, lakes, dykes, canals and slow-moving rivers, even brackish water.

Flight times
Mid June – late October, even into November in mild autumns.

Historical records
Dannreuther (1939) stated that it was "generally distributed and may become very common, due to migration". He was certainly correct in his prediction as it is now one of the most common species in the county and country. Chelmick's (1979) consideration that it is the "commonest Anisopteran in Sussex" is confirmed by this survey.

Conservation
Pollution and the over-shading of sites are the two main concerns. Males can be attracted by the provision of light-coloured, sun-bathing surfaces such as bare ground or stones. Larger habitat considerations include sunny hedgerows or woodland rides and clearings.

Ruddy Darter
Sympetrum sanguineum

This striking, bright crimson-red dragonfly has a more limited distribution than the Common Darter, but has been expanding its range in Sussex and elsewhere in the country. The male has a red-brown thorax and a bright, blood-red, 'waisted' abdomen with two black marks on segments 8 and 9. The female is dull yellow-brown overall with thin black lines along the sides of the abdomen.

▼ Immature male

▲ Male

National status
Resident in southern England and Wales, but extending its range.

Status in Sussex
Locally common across Sussex, but not nearly as widespread as the Common Darter. Concentrations of records occur on Pevensey Levels and Romney Marshes. Listed in the *Sussex Rare Species Inventory*.

Habitat
Well-vegetated ponds, lakes, gravel pits, canals and ditches, occasionally slow-flowing waters.

Flight times
Late June – late September.

Historical records
According to Dannreuther (1945) it was first recorded at Kingston near Lewes by W. Unwin in 1849. He also suggested that the species could die out if not reinforced by migration.

Chelmick (1979) considered the species to have been more common in East Sussex than in West, both historically and at the time of the 1965–1978 survey. He also noted that it "is one of the very few species to be found more abundantly on the Weald Clay and other neutral waters". Our survey indicates a wider range, in particular across the High Weald and on the South Coast Plain.

Conservation
Excessive plant clearance and dredging of ponds could be disastrous for this dragonfly, whose larvae spend their lives amongst the roots of aquatic vegetation. The strong populations in our grazing meadow ditch systems point to the continued need for sympathetic farming methods in these areas.

Female ▶

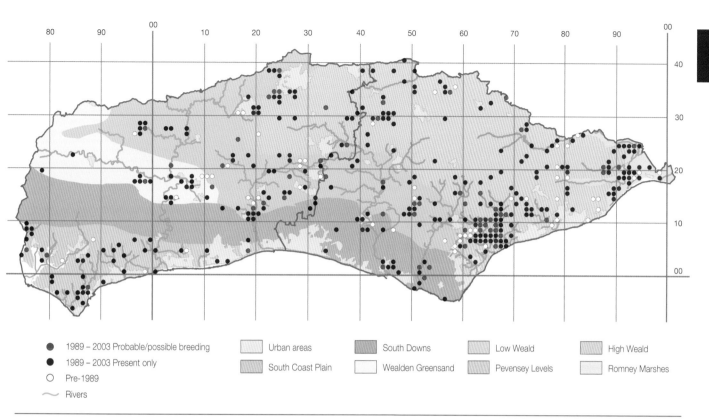

- ● 1989 – 2003 Probable/possible breeding
- ● 1989 – 2003 Present only
- ○ Pre-1989
- ～ Rivers

Urban areas	South Downs	Low Weald	High Weald
South Coast Plain	Wealden Greensand	Pevensey Levels	Romney Marshes

Black Darter
Sympetrum danae

Heathland pool, Trotton Common ▶

Our smallest dragonfly, only 32 mm long, the Black Darter is confined to acid heathland waters, but can occur in large numbers. It is a late summer species. The male is almost entirely black from the head and thorax to the slightly 'waisted' abdomen. The female is mainly yellow-brown with black markings on the sides of the abdomen. Colours are more variable in young and old individuals.

▲ Male   Mating ▶

National status
Widespread and can be abundant, especially in the north; local in eastern and central England.

Status in Sussex
Rare. Ashdown Forest and the Greensand heaths around Midhurst are the main haunts.

▼ Female

Habitat
Shallow, acidic pools on heathland, with a good range of aquatic and marginal vegetation.

Flight times
Mid July – early October, occasionally into November.

Historical records
Recorded at Ore, Hastings in 1900 by E. Butler (Dannreuther 1939) and at Frant on 2 and 6 October 1941 by Attlee (1942). However, by the 1965–1978 survey, the only records were for Wealden Greensand sites in the extreme northwest of the county (Chelmick 1979). Since then the species has apparently been spreading. Havers (1993) recorded the species at Buchan Ponds in 1992 (as did P. Belden) and at Holmbush Pond, Faygate in 1993. Curson (1998) also reported a sighting at Buchan in 1997 but failed to find any himself. On Ashdown Forest – for which Fowles (1985) had no records – Marrable (1999) found it at eight sites. Our survey also highlights its presence in other parts of the High Weald too.

Conservation
Conservation action should be directed to conserving and restoring our remaining heathland and providing more pools with the right balance of vegetation and open water. This is happening on Ashdown Forest, including in the Old Lodge reserve.

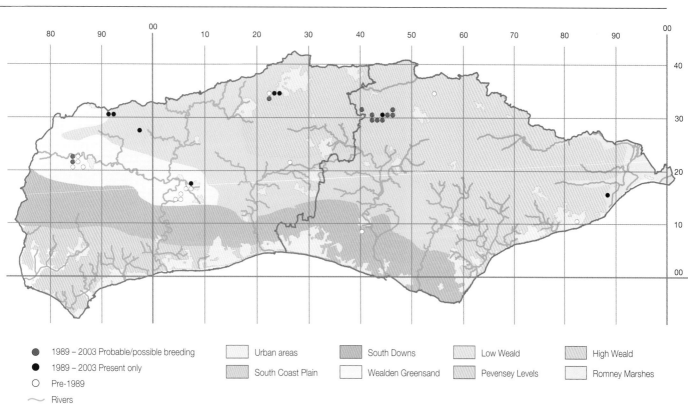

● 1989 – 2003 Probable/possible breeding
● 1989 – 2003 Present only
○ Pre-1989
~ Rivers

☐ Urban areas
▨ South Coast Plain
▨ South Downs
☐ Wealden Greensand
▨ Low Weald
▨ Pevensey Levels
▨ High Weald
☐ Romney Marshes

5 Species lost and won

Common Hawker female

As the climate and character of Sussex have changed over time, so too has the county's complement of dragonflies. One species has gone, some have made fleeting appearances and others are gradually establishing themselves or have done so briefly. The huge rise of interest in dragonflies means that recording now is far more thorough than ever before.

Sussex can claim the only British record of the Yellow-legged Clubtail (*Gomphus flavipes*), a species that breeds just over the Channel. One was taken near Hastings by J. Stephens on 5 August 1818 (Merritt *et al*. 1996).

Of several species there have been just two records. Those of the Scarce Blue-tailed Damselfly (*Ischnura pumilio*), common as near as the New Forest, were by S. Blenkarn, in May and July 1900 at Crowhurst and Abbots Wood, near Polegate, respectively (Dannreuther 1939). The Vagrant Darter (*Sympetrum vulgatum*) was found on Rye Marsh on 4 July 1966 and at Udimore six days later (*HESN*). Chelmick (1974) mentioned the Rye sightings, but later (Chelmick 1979) questioned them because no specimen had been taken. The sole record of White-faced Darter (*Leucorrhinia dubia*), by R. Palmer, is from Forest Mere Pond near Liphook in 1914 (Chelmick 1979).

The only breeding species known to have disappeared from Sussex is the Scarce Emerald Damselfly (*Lestes*

dryas), last recorded at Powdermill Reservoir by N. Moore on 11 August 1947 only seven years after its discovery. On 5 August 1940 he had found it on the Rother marshes near Bodiam (*HESN*) and there then followed regular reports by him and H. Attlee from Whatlington, Sedlescombe and Brede to the Rye coastal plain. By 1947 reports of this species had dwindled, partly because neither Moore nor Attlee continued to submit records to *HESN*. In 1978 Moore re-visited all the sites where he had previously found this species, but had no further sightings (Moore 1980) and Chelmick (1979), with similar results in the 1965–1978 survey, declared this species extinct in Sussex.

Perhaps no species poses such an obvious challenge to present day recorders as the Common Hawker (*Aeshna juncea*). Although common in western England, Wales and Scotland, there are few reports from Sussex. Due to lack of suitable habitat Chelmick (1979) questioned the

Beachy Head, a landfall for migrant dragonflies

70

Lesser Emperor male

Red-veined Darter male

Yellow-winged Darter male

validity of a record in the 1930s at Arundel where it was claimed to be "not uncommon". The 1965–1978 survey reported only two sites, both acid ponds bordering heathland in the extreme north-west of the county. Reports of the species in *HESN* for 1969, 1978–1981, 1985 and 1986 lack the details required now for RA70 recording forms. Blessed with the name of Common, it is perhaps not surprising that this species is frequently misidentified. Of the 15 records in the county only one has indicated any breeding behaviour, two ovipositing females at Forest Mere pond near Liphook noted by W. Merritt in 1975 (D. Chelmick pers. comm.).

Among new arrivals the largest species is the Lesser Emperor (*Anax parthenope*). The first records were of single insects at Rye Harbour on 23 and 27 July 1997 and 8 August 1998 found by P. Troake. Since then, there have been a further five sightings, stretching westwards to Cuckmere Haven; the most recent was on 26 August 2001, again at Rye.

Although Dannreuther (1939) listed it as a British but not a Sussex species, the Red-veined Darter (*Sympetrum fonscolombii*) had in fact been recorded in Sussex at Rye Harbour in 1898 by Lt Col. Irby (Chelmick 1974). N. Moore discovered one teneral female at Rye Harbour Gravel Pits in 1947, concluding that it had bred there (*HESN*), and the first confirmed

breeding record was of a larva found by P. Logan at Douster Pond (part of Buchan Hill Ponds) near Crawley on 29 June 1987 (Chelmick 1992). Since then, there have been a further 20 sightings. The best year was 2002 when individuals were seen at four separate, mainly coastal locations, including a remarkable five males seen by J. Atkinson and I. Whitcomb at Sheepcote Valley, Brighton on 17 July.

The Yellow-winged Darter (*Sympetrum flaveolum*) was first recorded in Sussex in the Hastings area from 12–15 September 1932 (Dannreuther 1939). There were further sightings at Rye Harbour by N. Moore in 1945, and large numbers followed in 1955, 1968, 1969 and 1973 (see Chelmick 1974, 1979). During the last well-documented influx into Britain, in August 1995, a total of 13 insects was recorded from coastal parts of the county (BDS Sussex Group data), apart from one at Hurston Warren. These records included an amazing 4 to 5 males and two females by P. Belden in his back garden in Brighton and two separate sightings on the same day (5 August) by T. Wilson – three males at Belle Tout Wood and one male and one female at Sheepcote Valley. The most recent records are in 2000 with singles appearing at Icklesham and Sheepcote Valley. Although the species has bred in Britain after such mass immigrations, breeding populations are normally short-lived and there is still no proof that this has happened in Sussex.

Although its "discovery" was recent (Parr 1994), the first county record for the Willow Emerald Damselfly (*Chalcolestes viridis*) dates back to 1979. D. Chelmick (pers. comm.) reports that an adult male was found dead on 22 September by D. Okines at Hankham clay pit, an old quarry on the edge of Glynleigh Level, near Pevensey. Although he himself visited the site – containing small to medium-sized pools dominated by rushes – Chelmick found no further specimens. Strangely enough the first Kent record of this species was also made retrospectively with the re-examination of an exuvia collected in 1992, but misidentified at the time (Brook and Brook 2003). Common just over the Channel, the Willow Emerald is a clear candidate for consolidating its status on British shores.

The Sussex scene for dragonflies will continue to change and offer challenges. The coastal position of the county, near to continental Europe, and its abundance of suitable habitats make it likely that other migrant species recorded elsewhere in Britain – like the Scarlet Darter (*Crocothemis erythraea*) and Southern Emerald Damselfly (*Lestes barbarus*) – will soon be added to its list, as well as new breeders following the example of the Small Red-eyed Damselfly. All that are needed is the enthusiasm to find them and the effort to submit the records to the Sussex Group of the BDS!

6 Conservation

One of the aims of recording dragonflies is to understand their distribution and to help conserve their habitats. During the survey work for this book the slowly accumulating data have been used on a number of occasions to make the conservation case for certain areas and, naturally, we hope that publication of the book itself will stimulate yet greater efforts. Many of the problems and opportunities facing dragonflies are symptomatic of those facing the wildlife and landscape of Sussex as a whole.

The condition of the county's aquatic environment – its streams, rivers, ponds and lakes – is heavily influenced by a number of factors: intensive agriculture, concentrations of industry, demands for water by an increasing population (leading to more abstraction from rivers and ground-water boreholes) and the gradually unravelling consequences of climate change, especially global warming. One of the roles of the Environment Agency (EA) is to monitor this condition. Analysis of maps on its website (www.environmentagency.org) shows that in the chemical quality of Sussex rivers "there has been a marked decline in the rate of improvement ... in recent years". Three reasons are given: greater volumes of discharge from sewage works (the River Ouse alone has 38); drought conditions as in 2001; and diffuse pollution from agricultural and urban run-off. For biological quality, an indicator of the overall 'health' of rivers, the picture is one of continuing improvement although quality "is unlikely to meet the standards required by the EC Water Framework Directive". The enrichment of water with nutrients such as nitrates and phosphate (eutrophication) can cause serious damage to invertebrates like dragonflies by reducing levels of dissolved oxygen. To prevent this, so-called nutrient-stripping plants have been introduced by the EA to designated sensitive areas such as Pevensey Levels.

It was on the Levels, the largest grazing meadows system in Sussex, that the first use was made of our dragonfly data. Following an initial report (Belden 1992) a detailed dragonfly survey was conducted as part of a systematic flora and fauna survey of the area. This helped the authorities and local land managers to improve the conservation of the Levels with a bespoke management scheme. In 1999 the area was declared a Wetland of International Importance under the Ramsar Convention. Time alone will test the statement of the then Chairman of English Nature, Baroness Young, that the ensuing management "benefits the farmers economically, wildlife prospers, and the site as a whole is conserved for future generations to enjoy – it is a good deal all round".

An alternative solution to combating the damaging effects of intensive farming promoted by the Common Agricultural Policy is through trial plots and demonstrations. The (West Sussex) Rother Landcare Project is encouraging local land managers to follow 'good practice' guidance and prevent soil erosion from the neighbouring sandy farmland and subsequent siltation of the river.

Protection of the environment needs to harness the combined strength of regulation, designation and individual site management.

The purchase of some of the county's key wetlands by conservation bodies has been important for dragonflies. The Sussex Wildlife Trust's acquisition of two fields enabled them to give evidence and win a public inquiry in March 1978 to prevent the draining of Amberley Wildbrooks on the floodplain of the River Arun. The Trust has subsequently bought more land here, and the Royal Society for the Protection of Birds now owns meadows upriver at Pulborough Brooks. The restoration of the area to traditional wet meadow management has benefited dragonflies as well as other wildlife, notably wetland birds. It is worth a trip to Romney Marsh in Kent to see what fate might have befallen Amberley; extensive drainage and dedication to intensive agriculture have led to an environment polluted and largely devoid of wildlife.

The loss of muddy, untidy, unmanaged farm ponds – including their replacement by clear-watered ones stocked with predatory fish – has no doubt had a heavy impact on the dragonfly fauna. Lakes too have their problems. In the case of Swanbourne Lake, used for ornamental boating on the Arundel Estate, the accumulated silt and organic matter had replaced much of the original water body, which was further depleted by abstraction from the chalk aquifer for local drinking water supply. During long, dry summers the lake would slowly dry out, leaving areas of the lake-bed exposed; the water was not then replenished until the wetter winter months. In 1998 investigations by the Environment Agency and Southern Water, working with Arundel Estate, concluded that the gradual silting up of the lake would eventually cause damage by permanently reducing the lake area. The lake had been dredged 60 years before when the material was deposited at the northern end. During 2002/2003 the lake was dredged in two phases (with the material spread on neighbouring agricultural land) and water abstraction reduced, to restore it to its former glory.

New opportunities for dragonflies are offered by sand and gravel extraction, a long-established industry in Sussex. Where the water table is suitable, new lakes have been made that are suitable both for water-based recreation and conservation; the gravel pits to the east of Chichester (clearly seen from the railway and A27) are good examples.

Not surprisingly, the species distribution maps for Sussex show the abundance of dragonflies in the river valleys. By contrast, few live on the South Downs. On the porous chalk shepherds of the past used to make dew ponds to water their stock in depressions in the clay cap. Conversion to arable cropping and the advent of piped water have made these downland oases agriculturally redundant so the Sussex Downs Conservation Board has led a programme to restore them. The clay has been 're-puddled' or supplemented beneath with a plastic liner to prevent the ponds drying out.

In a few places, new ponds have been created, helping dragonflies as well as other wildlife.

Recreational activities can have an impact on wildlife. Of all outdoor pursuits, fishing is the most popular in Britain so ensuring that the management of fisheries is sympathetic to wildlife is clearly important. On the River Arun erosion of the banks due to the wash of speed-boats has been a growing concern with the authorities, and there are periodic patrols to catch and prosecute the culprits. Many golf clubs are now advocating the use of fewer chemicals and a more sensitive mowing regime for fairways and roughs. Hurston Warren Golf Course, West Chiltington is a fabulous acid grassland course, with some rich wetland habitat, supporting the Small Red Damselfly. Dew ponds have also been restored on several downland golf courses, such as at Pyecombe, and Blatchington, Seaford. There are also changes with canals, often valuable habitats for a wide variety of aquatic plants and animals, and among the more accessible places to see our more common dragonflies. In the course of its own restoration and operation work the Wey and Arun Canal Trust, for example, lists nature conservation among its objectives.

Climate change and global warming will be introducing new changes to the Sussex environment for dragonflies. One consequence has been the immigration of some species from mainland Europe (see p.71). Another is a rise in sea level (ca. 0.5 m before the end of the century) that is challenging

traditional attitudes to keeping the sea at bay. At Cuckmere Haven, a policy of 'planned retreat' is emerging with the creation of an intertidal habitat with salt marshes. For dragonflies, mostly averse to brackish water, the greater benefits may accrue inland where management of our river systems is increasingly looking to using low-lying areas as 'sponges', soaking up water (and creating a range of freshwater habitats) and slowly releasing it rather than channelling flood water to the sea as quickly as possible. Memories of the recent catastrophic floods of Chichester, Lewes and Uckfield are still strong and make these plans more pressing.

Whatever developments do take place in Sussex, they must incorporate water conservation and enhancement measures, from which dragonflies (and other wildlife) could benefit. For example, sustainable urban drainage systems, instead of piping rainwater away seawards, could divert it back to aquifers or re-create surface water courses. Increasing demand for water, allied to the recent trend of hotter and drier summers, may lead to the construction of new reservoirs. Well-designed ones could be attractive for certain species, but inevitably other habitats like streams and ponds may be destroyed.

No group of insects can give us a better, more spectacular indicator of the aquatic health of the environment than dragonflies. A future edition of this book will hopefully indicate that their abundance and diversity are greater than they are now – and that Sussex is a better place for it.

Tale of an enthusiast's new garden pond

'A wildlife garden without a pond is like a theatre without a stage', declared Chris Baines in his classic book *How to make a wildlife garden*, and this phrase was the inspiration behind my digging a pond early in 2002. Our home is near Lewes, at the base of the South Downs, fully one mile from the nearest main water source, so it would hardly be regarded as prime dragonfly habitat. However, our oasis, a mere 8ft x 6ft and 2ft deep, attracted nine species of dragonfly in its first summer, boosting the records at the Biodiversity Record Centre from nothing to nine species for our 1 km square. I was also fortunate to see eight of them laying eggs, so look forward to many emergences over the coming years.

Digging a pond is really extremely simple. The BDS booklet *Digging a pond for dragonflies* provides all the information you need. It is worth taking time over the planning. Spend as long as you need marking out the proposed area, then changing it until you are happy with the shape and location. Visit your local water centres to get the best deal on the thickest rubber liner, then set aside a day to dig the hole. Commence by removing strips of turf, then dig the hole, allowing a shallow shelf at the south-west corner. Remove all sharp stones. If your pond is small, the sides will be fairly steep, so you may find that the sand laid to protect against punctures will not stay in place and will be better replaced by fibreglass insulation. To anchor the liner, dig a shallow trench around the edge and then place the soil back over the liner. Replace the turves over the trench, which should just reach the pond edge and hide the black rubber. The trench could also be flooded and filled with marginal plants. At last you are ready to fill with water.

Our pond was filled with water on 17 May. The next step was to purchase a variety of native water-plants – Water Violet, Water Milfoil, Brooklime, Lesser Spearwort, Fringed Water-lily and Bogbean – and taking care to avoid those exotic species (still sold by the horticultural trade) that are now clogging up our ponds and lakes, such as Australian Swamp Stonecrop, Parrot's Feather and Water Fern. Within ten days a pair of Large Red Damselflies had arrived, followed by Azure and Blue-tailed Damselflies. If you wish to give your pond a kick-start, borrow a bucket of silt from the bottom of a friend's pond or you can do as I did, which is to wait and see what happens naturally.

June 27 was a key date marking the appearance of the first true dragonfly, a Broad-bodied Chaser. He made several circuits before perching on the Lesser Spearwort. Upon our return from a fortnight away, a female Broad-bodied Chaser was seen egg-laying. The following day, the first Common Darter appeared, followed two weeks later by a female Emperor. At the end of August, the stage was set alight by six darters – four Ruddy and two Common – plus occasional flurries by a Migrant Hawker. The ferocity of the aerial combats resounded around the garden, resulting at one point in one darter flying directly into our sitting-room window. It was momentarily stunned, but then shook itself and returned to the fray. The arrival of our daughter and her husband from New Zealand prompted even more interesting behaviour, as a female Southern Hawker took a liking to Tony and actually landed upon him. Tony was happy with his own mate so beat a hasty retreat. Throughout the summer, we were visited by a variety of dragonflies as long as the weather was warm. Twelve o'clock appeared to be their favourite time. This continued until our final Common Darter was seen on 26 October.

Detailed observation may be made with a monocular or close-focusing binoculars when in the garden, but it requires a degree of cunning and slow movement, as you will soon be aware that a pair of beady eyes are watching your every movement, ready to take off, if you venture just a bit too near. The pond is also an attraction to other wildlife. Apart from the expected pond-skaters and diving beetles, we receive occasional visits from Linnets, Goldfinches, Grey Wagtails and our ever-present Greenfinches.

During the winter, I bought a pond-dipping net. This confirmed the

Ponds are magnets for children as well as dragonflies! This one is at the Sussex Wildlife Trust headquarters at Woods Mill

presence of both Emperor and Large Red Damselflies, but at such an early stage it is difficult to be precise on identification as the various species go through up to fifteen larval stages. To supplement my larvae identification knowledge, I attended a one day course run by the National Dragonfly Project team at Wicken Fen – great fun and highly recommended.

Final confirmation of successful breeding was achieved on 11 May 2003, with the emergence of a Broad-bodied Chaser. It crawled up the pond-liner, crossed a patch of lawn over a flower-bed and proceeded to climb vertically half-way up our fence-post. Over the next two hours, it emerged despite the rather cool and

wet weather. It was remarkable to watch as it used its fluid firstly to fill its wings and then its abdomen, becoming twice the size of the insect that emerged from its shell. The next morning, we found it on the ground and, having persuaded it on to my finger, I moved it into the hedgerow on the other side of the garden, further away from the bird-feeders. It remained there until the morning after when it flew off into the distance. Finally, 2004 got off to a flying start with the emergence of two Large Red Damselflies on 26 April, then an Emperor Dragonfly exuvia, discovered on the morning of 19 May, was followed the next morning by the sight of an emerged adult hanging on to its exuvia. I watched it for fully an hour,

until the sun had warmed it up sufficiently. When I moved, it took off and flew away at 7.40 am, only to return to the same perch for a further five minutes to strengthen its wings. These glistened in the sun as it took off in the direction of the nearby fields. The Emperor emergence totalled 13 insects, confirmed by the evidence of exuviae, and lasted from 19–31 May.

If you haven't got a pond, don't delay. Start digging today. You will not regret it. You can always use the excess soil to start building that rock-garden you always promised yourself.

John Luck

8 Good sites to visit

If you are new to dragonflies, or simply want to expand your horizons, try visiting the sites below, all of which have easy access. Use Ordnance Survey maps, and the grid references, to find them and to see a selection of some of the species likely to occur there through the season.

Abbots Wood Lake
Signposted off the A27 west of Polegate at the Wilmington crossroads. Forest Enterprise car park (TQ 558073).

Large Red, Red-eyed, Azure, and Blue-tailed Damselflies, Southern Hawker, Hairy Dragonfly, Broad-bodied Chaser, Black-tailed Skimmer.

Amberley Wildbrooks
Limited parking in Amberley village (TQ 030133). The Wildbrooks and a right of way are accessed down a chalky lane, north of the village. A public footpath (wide track) leads north across the brooks, meeting numerous ditches.

Banded Demoiselle, Variable and Hairy Dragonflies, Four-spotted Chaser.

Bines Bridge, River Adur
South of Partridge Green on the B2135, with ample parking at the bridge (TQ 189176). A footpath runs north along the east bank of the river although access can be difficult along the bank in places.

Banded Demoiselle, White-legged and Red-eyed Damselflies, Emperor and Hairy Dragonflies, Scarce Chaser.

Boreham Bridge
Between Boreham Street and Ninfield on the A271. Some roadside parking (TQ 676120). Walk south alongside Waller's Haven/Moorhall Stream.

Banded Demoiselle, Emerald, Large Red, Red-eyed, Azure, Variable, Common Blue and Blue-tailed Damselflies, Migrant and Brown Hawkers, Emperor and Hairy Dragonflies, Broad-bodied Chaser, Black-tailed Skimmer, Common and Ruddy Darters.

Burton Pond
East of the A285 Duncton to Petworth road, small parking area by ex-mill (SU 978180); for buses, ring Traveline 0870 6082608. Nature trail, marked by dragonfly arrows, guides you round the lake.

Demoiselles, Emerald, Large Red, Red-eyed and Blue Damselflies, Migrant, Southern and Brown Hawkers, Golden-ringed Dragonfly, Downy Emerald, Four-spotted, Scarce and Broad-bodied Chasers, Common and Ruddy Darters.

Chichester Canal
An unspoilt canal, with a good towpath. From Chichester railway station, canal is a two-minute walk to the south (SU 858042). Towpath access (on foot) all the way, via Hunston, to Birdham yacht basin and estuary of Chichester Harbour [SU 827012]. Also, car park at Hunston (SU 865023).

Azure, Common Blue and Blue-tailed Damselflies, Emperor and Hairy Dragonflies.

Chichester Gravel Pits
This is the largest collection of inland water habitat in West Sussex. The pits have some public footpaths, but some of the complex is not publicly accessible. Roadside car parking on the B2145 by the public bridleway (SU 868036).

Similar species to Chichester Canal, with Black-tailed Skimmer present in large numbers.

Michelham Priory
Remains of 13th Century Priory embraced by a moat and the Cuckmere River. Ample car parking (TQ 556093).

Banded Demoiselle, Emerald, Large Red, Red-eyed, Azure, Common Blue and Blue-tailed Damselflies, Migrant and Brown Hawkers, Emperor and Hairy Dragonflies, Common Darter.

New Bridge, River Arun
On the A272 between Billingshurst and Wisborough Green (at TQ 069260). Limited parking. There is good access both north and south alongside the River Arun and the old Wey and Arun Canal.

Banded Demoiselle, White-legged and Red-eyed Damselflies, Emperor, Hairy and Club-tailed Dragonflies, Scarce Chaser.

Old Lodge
This Sussex Wildlife Trust reserve is high in the heart of the Ashdown Forest. Its series of small pools holds characteristic, and some of them rare, acid water species. There is parking just outside the reserve (TQ470305) and nearby.

Small Red Damselfly, Migrant, Southern and Brown Hawkers, Emperor and Golden-ringed Dragonflies, Broad-bodied Chaser, Keeled Skimmer, Black Darter.

Pevensey Levels
A large area criss-crossed by limited public footpaths. A good map may be needed. Footpaths include: a) from the Lamb Inn on the A259 (TQ 676081), north and south of road, following and crossing minor ditches; b) from the A259 at Pevensey Bay (TQ 650036) north to Pevensey Castle (alongside Langney Sewer for a short distance); c) north from the Star Inn, Norman's Bay (TQ 686060), along Waller's Haven, but the footpath is unmapped and the bridge may be missing; and d) east of the Star Inn, following and crossing minor ditches.

Emerald, Variable and Red-eyed Damselflies, Four-spotted Chaser.

Seven Sisters Country Park and Cuckmere River
There are two car parks at the Countryside Centre on A259 at Exceat east of Seaford (TV 518995) and just inland, along the Litlington Road, there is a Forest Enterprise car park (TQ 518002). The rides in Friston Forest provide ideal roosting habitat and are excellent for late season species (Anisoptera) on warm autumn days.

Emerald, Large Red, Azure and Blue-tailed Damselflies, Migrant, Southern and Brown Hawkers, Emperor Dragonfly, Four-spotted and Broad-bodied Chasers, Black-tailed Skimmer, Common Darter.

Slaugham Pond
This tree-fringed lake is a half-mile west of Slaugham village near Handcross and has easy parking and all-round access (TQ 250282).

Brown Hawker, Downy and Brilliant Emeralds, Black-tailed Skimmer.

Wakehurst Place
The lowest parts of the grounds of this National Trust-owned but Kew-run garden (TQ 342317) north of Ardingly

A dragonfly sculpture, one metre across, in central Brighton

contain a lake and so-called Reed Swamp, connected by a stream, and leading into the northern extremity of Ardingly Reservoir. A walkway across the Swamp offers excellent views of dragonflies.

White-legged and Red-eyed Damselflies, Migrant and Brown Hawkers, Brilliant Emerald, Ruddy Darter.

Woods Mill
The headquarters of the Sussex Wildlife Trust on the A2037 south of Henfield has free access and parking for members (TQ 218137).

Banded Demoiselle, Red-eyed and Azure Damselflies, Brown Hawker, Emperor and Hairy Dragonflies, Broad-bodied Chaser.

9 Want to know more?

This section offers some advice on how to expand your interest in dragonflies.

Useful contacts

Booth Museum of Natural History, 194 Dyke Road, Brighton BN1 5AA. Regular exhibitions and events; local information and records centre. www.booth.virtualmuseum.info.

British Dragonfly Society, The Secretary, The Haywain, Hollywater Road, Bordon, Hampshire GU35 0AD. www.dragonflysoc.org.uk. The only UK society devoted entirely to the study and conservation of dragonflies. It maintains a nationwide recording scheme, publishes the *Journal of the British Dragonfly Society* and a newsletter, and promotes regional walks and talks. There are many local groups such as our one here in Sussex. The website contains much invaluable information.

English Nature, The regional office covering south-east England is at Phoenix House, 32–33 North Street, Lewes, East Sussex BN7 2PH. www.english-nature.org.uk.

The Environment Agency emergency hotline telephone number for reporting pollution, illegal fishing, dumping etc. is 0800 807060. The website www.environmentagency.org has information pages called State of the Environment.

Sussex Biodiversity Record Centre, c/o Sussex Wildlife Trust. Keeper of Sussex's wildlife information and surveys, plus contact point for recorders. www.sxbrc.org.uk.

Sussex Wildlife Trust, Woods Mill, Henfield, West Sussex BN5 9SD. The county naturalists' trust, with many nature reserves and some regional walks, talks and other events. www.wildlifetrust.org.uk/sussex.

Useful literature

Atropos. Describes itself as the "UK's premier journal for Lepidoptera and Odonata enthusiasts". www.atropos.co.uk.

British Dragonfly Society. 1993. *Managing habitats for dragonflies*.

British Dragonfly Society. n.d. *Dig a pond for dragonflies*.

Brooks S, 2002. *Field guide to the dragonflies and damselflies of Great Britain and Ireland*. Revised edition. British Wildlife Publishing, Rotherwick, Hampshire. Perhaps the best identification guide, with outstanding artwork by Richard Lewington.

Brooks, S. and Askew, R. 1999. *A guide to the dragonflies and damselflies of Britain*. Publication no. OP53. Field Studies Council, Preston Montford, Shrewsbury. An excellent pull-out chart with illustrations. www.field-studies-council.org.

Merritt R., Moore N.W. and Eversham B.C. 1996. *Atlas of the dragonflies of Britain and Ireland*. ITE Research Publication no. 9. HMSO, London. The definitive work on the subject, but out of print.

Powell, D. 1999. *A guide to the dragonflies of Great Britain*. Arlequin Press, Chelmsford. Unusual, but nevertheless useful guide to the British species. Beautiful watercolour paintings of species, highlighting key identification features and "jizz."

Smallshire, D. and Swash, A. 2004. *Britain's dragonflies*. WILDGuides, Old Basing. Covers 44 breeding, 3 extinct, 10 vagrant and 6 potential vagrant species, with photo montages.

Code of Practice

The British Dragonfly Society has produced a code of practice for its members. A modified summary is reproduced here, which we trust is followed by everyone who reads this book and wishes to further their enjoyment of these wonderful insects.

Principle 1: *Live dragonflies should only be held captive for good reasons.*

Identification and other inspection can normally be done by observation, photography and collecting exuviae (larval skins), aided by a good reference guide. If necessary, for close inspection, it is possible to capture adult and larval dragonflies, examine them and release them undamaged. Live specimens should only be collected under expert supervision. Releases should be at the sites where the species were found.

Principle 2: *Dragonflies should only be killed when a justifiable and useful purpose is served thereby.*

This activity should not, in the main, be carried out. This principle is relevant to professionals and other experts, when proof of a species is needed or for well-planned and justified scientific research.

Askew, R. 2004. *The dragonflies of Europe*. Revised paperback edition. Harley Books, Great Horkesley, Colchester.

Belden, P.A. 1987. *Pevensey Levels dragonflies*. Report for East Sussex County Council and Nature Conservancy Council.

Belden, P.A. 1992. *Pevensey Levels – dragonflies*. Report to the National Rivers Authority.

Belden, P.A. 1994. *Pevensey Levels dragonfly survey 1993–4.* Report to National Rivers Authority.

Belden, P.A. 1995. *Report on the status of dragonflies, A259 Road Corridor, Pevensey Levels, A259 Pevensey – Bexhill Proposed Road Developments.*

Belden, P.A. 1999. *Dragonflies of the Arun Valley*. Internal report to Arun District Council on behalf of Sussex Group, British Dragonfly Society.

Bloomfield, E.N. 1900. Odonata of East Sussex. *Entomologists Monthly Magazine* XI: 150.

Bloomfield, E.N. 1910. Notes on the local fauna & flora. *Hastings and East Sussex Naturalist* 1: 209.

Brook, J. and Brook, G. 2001. *Dragonflies of Kent*. Transactions of Kent Field Club 16. Kent Field Club. [No location but available from http://www.nhbs.co.uk.]

Brook, J. and Brook, G. 2003. The Willow Emerald dragonfly *Chalcolestes viridis* (Vander Linden) in Kent: a case of mistaken identity. *Journal of the British Dragonfly Society* 19: 51–54.

Cham, S. 2003. Factors influencing the distribution of the White-legged Damselfly *Platycnemis pennipes* (Pallas) in Great Britain. *Journal of the British Dragonfly Society* 19: 15–23.

Chelmick, D.G. 1974. The dragonflies of Rye Harbour, 1974. *Rye Harbour Nature Reserve Annual Report for 1975*: 5-8.

Chelmick, D.G. 1979. *A survey of the Odonata of Sussex (1965–1978).* Internal document produced on behalf of the Sussex Wildlife Trust.

Chelmick, D.G. 1997. The rediscovery of *Ceriagrion tenellum* (De Villers) in West Sussex. *Journal of the British Dragonfly Society* 13: 24–26.

Craven, A.E. 1922. Sussex dragon-flies. *Hastings and East Sussex Naturalist* 3 (1918–1923): 204–210.

Curson, J. 1998. *Survey of Buchan Hill Ponds SSSI*. West Sussex County Council and English Nature.

Dannreuther, T. 1939. The dragonflies of East Sussex, 1939. *Hastings and East Sussex Naturalist* 5: 274–278.

Dannreuther, T. 1941. A preliminary note on dragonfly migration. *South-eastern Union of Scientific Societies*; reprinted in *Annual Report for 1941*: 63–65.

Dannreuther, T. 1945. *Dragonflies of West Sussex*, 1945. Supplement to *Proceedings of the Natural Science and Archaeology Society, Littlehampton*, 1939–1945.

Dewick, S. and Gerussi, R. 2000. Small Red-eyed Damselfly *Erythromma viridulum* (Charpentier) found breeding in Essex – the first British records. *Atropos* 9: 3–4.

Follett, P. 1996. *Dragonflies of Surrey.* Surrey Wildlife Trust, Pirbright.

Fowles, A.P. 1985. *A site survey for the conservation of Odonata on the Ashdown Forest Commons*. Internal report for Conservators of Ashdown Forest.

Furley, G.M. 1931. Odonata. Some dragonflies seen in the district. *Natural Science and Archaeology Society, Littlehampton: Reports of Proceedings,* 1931–1932: 21.

Griffiths, P.A. 1994. *Report on the status and distribution of species of Odonata in the River Arun catchment.* National Rivers Authority.

Havers, J. 1999. *Dragonflies in the Crawley area, 1996*. Internal report for West Sussex County Council.

Hastings and East Sussex Naturalist (*HESN*). [The source of many records, for example those of H.G. Attlee and N.W. Moore.]

Hunter, I. 2003. Reports from Coastal Stations – 2002; Elms Farm, Icklesham, East Sussex. *Atropos* 18: 55–56.

Iles, I.S. 1998. An investigation into the affects of bank collapse and cattle trample on Odonata species at Okehurst on the River Arun, West Sussex. *Journal of the British Dragonfly Society* 14: 14–20.

Longfield, C. 1937. *The dragonflies of the British Isles*. Warne, London and New York.

Lucas, W.J. 1900. *British dragonflies (Odonata)*. Upcott Gill, London.

Lucas, W.J. and Bloomfield, E.N. 1905. Odonata. In Page, A., *The Victoria County History of Sussex,* Vol. 1, pp. 115–116. Constable, London. Reprinted 1973 by Dawsons, Folkestone for the Institute of Historical Research, University of London.

Marrable, C.J. 1999. *A survey of sites suitable for damselflies and dragonflies on Ashdown Forest, 1999.* Internal report for Conservators of Ashdown Forest.

Merrifield, Mrs. 1860. *A sketch of the natural history of Brighton and its vicinity*. W. Pearce, Brighton. Reprinted by H. & C. Teacher, London. [Odonata on pp. 153, 223.]

Merritt R., Moore N.W. and Eversham B.C. 1996. *Atlas of the dragonflies of Britain and Ireland*. ITE Research Publication no. 9. HMSO, London.

Moore, N.W. 1980. *Lestes dryas* Kirby – a declining species of dragonfly in need of conservation: notes on its status and habitat in England and Ireland. *Biological Conservation* 17: 143–148.

Parr, A.J. 1996. Dragonfly movement and migration in Britain and Ireland. *Journal of the British Dragonfly Society* 12: 33–50.

Parr, A.J. 2004. Migrant dragonflies in the 21st century. *Darter* 21: 4–5.

Rye Harbour Report 1999. [Section on dragonflies, p. 53.] East Sussex County Council.

Ryland, K. 1994. *The Wey and Arun Canal restoration. An ecological appraisal.* Dolphin Ecological Surveys for English Nature.

Silsby, J. and Ward-Smith, J. 1997. The influx of *Sympetrum flaveolum* (L.) during the summer of 1995. *Journal of the British Dragonfly Society* 13: 14–22.

Taverner, J., Cham, S. and Hold, A. 2004. *The dragonflies of Hampshire.* Pisces Publications, Newbury.

Unwin, W.C. 1853. Libellulinae observed in Sussex, chiefly in the neighbourhood of Lewes. *The Naturalist* July: 71–73.